Topics in Mathematics for the Tenth Grade

Based on teaching practices in Waldorf schools

Topics in Mathematics for the Tenth Grade

Based on teaching practices in Waldorf schools

Trigonometry
Sequences and Series
Arithmetic and Geometric Means
Exponents
Logarithms
Exponential Equations
Continued Fractions
Landscape Surveying

Peter Baum, Arnold Bernhard, Karl-F. Georg, Uwe Hansen, Markus Hünig,
H.-Christian Ohlendorf, Marcus v. Schwanenflügel, Jürgen Vogt
Translated by John Caughman, Editor: Robert Neumann

Published by the Lesson Plan Initiative of the Pedagogical Research Center in Kassel
in cooperation with
Waldorf Publications and the Research Institute for Waldorf Education
Printed with the support of the Waldorf Curriculum Fund

www.lehrerseminar-forschung.de
www.waldorfbuch.de
www.waldorfpublications.org

Impressum

© Bildungswerk Beruf und Umwelt

1. Edition 10-10-2008
Reprinted 1-10-2016
Typesetting: Robert Neumann, Freiburg
Printed by Waldorf Publications

Contents

Preface

In March 1994, a preliminary edition booklet appeared with the title *Topics in Mathematics for the 9th and 10th Grades*, published by the Pädagogischen Forschungsstelle, Abteilung Kassel. It appeared in 1999 in a revised edition with additional articles, but was limited to topics for the 9th grade. The article *Trigonometry in the 10th Grade*, by Arnold Bernhard, was incorporated without changes into the current booklet *Topics in Mathematics for the 10th Grade*. All of the remaining articles in this booklet, however, are new to this edition. While they are primarily intended as a resource for new teachers, they can also provide useful enrichment for colleagues who have more teaching experience. Several of these articles, derived from the teaching practices of the authors, have already appeared in a preliminary edition in 2001. These have now been corrected, revised, and expanded through further articles and this preface.

The authors have convened about four times annually to discuss the content of mathematical instruction in Waldorf schools. In such work, there is sometimes a risk of over-focusing on the task of preparing students for standardized testing or for the requirements of a particular diploma. Of course, such standards must be met. But the engagement of a student with mathematics carries a much deeper significance: unlike almost any other school activity, it has the ability to empower the student with faith in their own reasoning. This requires not only specific content, but also specific teaching methods. The latter could only be discussed peripherally in this booklet. In addition to topics for mathematics lessons in the 11th grade – which will be treated in a next volume – it would be desirable to have a description of the various teaching methods and their emphases in the everyday classroom. This would be particularly useful because, unfortunately, when *poorly* implemented, mathematics instruction can cause faith in one's own reasoning to be destroyed, rather than fostered.

The authors of these essays welcome your critique and suggestions.

Special thanks are due to Mr. Juergen Garbe, Dipl.-Ing., for his painstaking transcription of the individual texts and for the placement of the numerous diagrams, and to Ms. Sabine Scherer for the final editing.

Peter Baum

September 2002

Preface to the English Edition

The "green books" of the series "Mathematics for the High School" from Kassel have been a great help and support to high school teachers for years. Not only are they useful when one is trying to familiarize oneself with teaching in a Waldorf school, but they are also a source of inspiration – offering fresh perspectives or new insights into courses that have been taught many times.

At a number of conferences it has become clear that there exists a great interest in material for the high school curriculum among the non-german-speaking participants. More often than not, however, attempts to work with german books have failed as a result of the language barrier.

Thus was born the idea to translate these books for high school into English. Because the focus of the high school professional development week in Kassel in the coming year will be the 10th grade – and because this event will take place in English for the first time – this book was the natural place to begin. We hope that in this way, the essays can be read by many who are interested in them, and that their instruction can be thereby enriched accordingly.

Special thanks go to Prof. Dr. John Caughman for this translation.

Robert Neumann

September 2008

Some Anthroposophical and Methodological Views, Developed through Examples

Uwe Hansen

As they enter the upper grades, high school students have a desire to explore bold new ways of thinking, to discover new things with joy.

In the subsequent years, students would like to connect even more to these new thoughts, and to understand more deeply that which they have previously learned. They develop a sense for the harmony, the beauty, and the naturalness of a proof.

They want to understand details from a broader context.

Just as *Goethe* wanted to understand individual specific plants in terms of his primitive Urplants – the part proceeding from the whole – so it must also be possible to develop mathematical contexts so that the specific is formed out of a unifying whole.

This is evident in the way one can sense, in every mathematical statement, a desire for generalization. One would like the concrete case to fall into a comprehensive scheme of regularity. One frees oneself thereby from particular assumptions and finds oneself in an abstract domain. From this domain, the specific cases appear in a special light.

In high school, the young person tries to recognize the core of his being, to grasp the center of his being. Gaining familiarity with the various types of mathematical means – arithmetic, geometric, and harmonic – can be of use to him in this endeavor; every construction of a mean is a quest for symmetry, in that two quantities must be so viewed that they appear in a harmonic relationship through a "mean" value.

The arithmetic mean $m = \frac{1}{2}(a+b)$ of the two quantities a and b is the template for the construction of all means. It can also be viewed, however, as a special case of the harmonic mean. This will be made clear through the following geometric presentation.

Upon a segment AB, the Thales circle is constructed having AB as its diameter. From a point P on the line AB but outside the circle, both tangent lines to the circle are drawn. The line segment joining the two points of tangency cuts the segment AB in a point Q (Fig. 1).

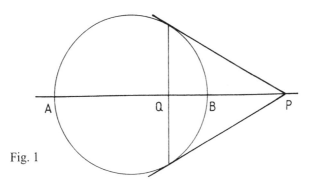

Fig. 1

One refers to *PQ* as the harmonic mean of *PA* and *PB*. As *P* tends toward a point infinitely far from the line *AB*, the point *Q* tends toward the midpoint of *AB*, whose coordinates then are given by the arithmetic means of the coordinates of points *A* and *B*.

This connection shows that the construction of means is closely associated with the relationship between interior and exterior, that the proportions in the interior of a segment cannot be conceived as independent from the proportions in the exterior an experience that is certainly of great significance for young people.

The surprising fact is that the point *Q* divides the segment *AB* internally in the same way that the point *P* divides it externally. So the segments satisfy *AQ* : *QB* = *AP* : *PB*. One says that these four points lie in harmonic position.

The special symmetry of this harmonic division shows itself, in that, not only do the points *Q* and *P* divide the segment *AB* in equal proportions, but also the points *A* and *B* divide the segment *PQ* in equal proportions. That is why *AB* is also the harmonic mean of *AQ* and *AP*.

Without using the circle, one can also arrive at the point *Q* from point *P* by drawing lines through each of *A* and *B* that intersect each other at *S*. Construct a line through *P* that intersects *AS* in a point *R* and *BS* in a point *T*. The line through *S* and the intersection of *AT* with *BR* then meets *AB* at the point *Q*.

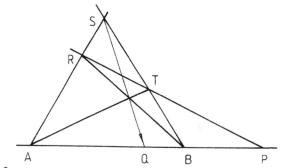

Fig. 2

This discussion shows that the harmonic position – or harmonic division – is associated with the basic elements of geometry.

If we denote the length of segment *PA* by *a*, of *PB* by *b*, and of *PQ* by *m*, then we obtain from the fact that *PB* : *BQ* = *PA* : *AQ* the equation *b* : (*m* − *b*) = *a* : (*a* − *m*), or

$$\frac{1}{m} = \frac{1}{2}\left(\frac{1}{a} + \frac{1}{b}\right) \qquad m = \frac{2ab}{a+b}.$$

This mean value *m* determines, therefore, the harmonic mean of *a* and *b*. Because *AB* is the harmonic mean of *AQ* and *AP*, it also holds that

$$\frac{1}{a-b} = \frac{1}{2}\left(\frac{1}{a-m} + \frac{1}{a}\right).$$

We note an additional perspective from the theory of music:

The musical fifth is the harmonic mean between a tone and its octave, i.e., $\frac{2}{3}$ is the harmonic mean of 1 and $\frac{1}{2}$.

The major third is the harmonic mean between a tone and its fifth, i.e., $\frac{4}{5}$ is the harmonic mean of 1 and $\frac{2}{3}$.

The major second is the harmonic mean between a tone and its third, i.e., $\frac{8}{9}$ is the harmonic mean of 1 and $\frac{4}{5}$.

This can be seen in the following diagram.

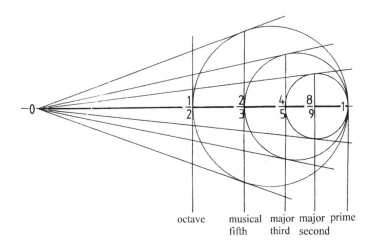

| octave | musical fifth | major third | major second | prime |

Generally, the following holds:

$$\frac{2^{n+1}}{2^{n+1}+1} \text{ is the harmonic mean between 1 and } \frac{2^n}{2^n+1}$$

For $n = 0, 1, 2$, one obtains the aforementioned special cases.

Every segment has a midpoint; but one cannot speak of a "harmonic midpoint" of a segment. This is because the endpoints alone do not determine the harmonic mean, but also a further reference point. One can, however, speak of a mean in reference to any given "exterior point".

In introducing the harmonic mean, it was assumed that the point P lies outside the segment AB. If P lies in the interior, then the construction proceeds in reverse. Then the harmonic mean will lie outside the segment AB. In this case negative numbers will appear. Three examples will illustrate this:

The harmonic mean of 4 and 12 is 6;

$$6 = \frac{2 \cdot 4 \cdot 12}{4 + 12}$$

$$PB = 4$$
$$PA = 12$$
$$PQ = 6$$

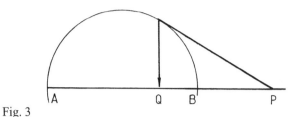

Fig. 3

The harmonic mean of -4 and 2 is 8;

$$8 = \frac{2 \cdot (-4) \cdot 2}{-4 + 2}$$

$$\begin{aligned} PA &= -4 \\ PB &= 2 \\ PQ &= 8 \end{aligned}$$

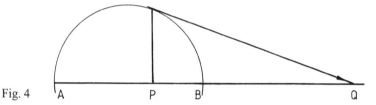

Fig. 4

The harmonic mean of 6 and -2 is -6;

$$-6 = \frac{2 \cdot (-2) \cdot 6}{6 + (-2)}$$

$$\begin{aligned} PA &= -2 \\ PB &= 6 \\ PQ &= -6 \end{aligned}$$

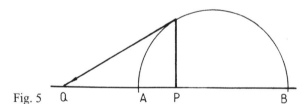

Fig. 5

If we treat a as a variable and b as a constant, then the mean proportion between a and b varies in a particularly characteristic manner.

Four points $ABPQ$ in harmonic position stand in a noteworthy relation to the circular arc. If C is any given point on the Thales circle constructed on diameter AB, then it is always the case that $\angle QCB = \angle BCP$, i.e.: from the point C, the segments QB and BP subtend equal angles. The circle itself is the geometric locus of all points from which two collinear segments that share an endpoint subtend equal angles – this holds even when the segments do not touch. In the case when the two segments are of equal length, this geometric locus is simply the perpendicular bisector.

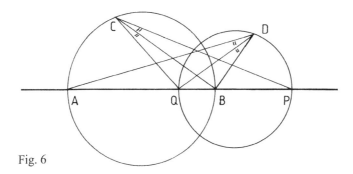

Fig. 6

Whenever the points *P* and *Q* divide the segment *AB* internally and externally into an equal angle proportions, it will also be the case that the points *A* and *B* divide the segment *PQ* internally and externally into the same proportions. That means that equality of angles holds for two circles: the Thales circle constructed on diameter *AB* and the Thales circle constructed on *QP*. Therefore if *D* is any given point on the Thales circle constructed on diameter *QP*, then $\angle ADQ = \angle QDB$.

When *C* and *D* meet, that is, when the intersection point *S* of the two Thales circles is considered, then the angles *ASB* and *QSP* must be bisected by each other's legs. Because the angles *ASB* and *QSP* are both 90°, it follows that a 45° angle must appear four times.

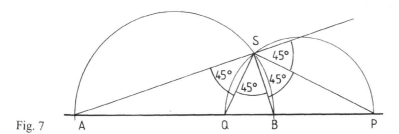

Fig. 7

Through the intersection of the two circles, the harmonic position of four points on a line is condensed in this way to an exact quadrisection of an angle.

The harmonic mean can now also be seen in a surprising relationship to the geometric mean (or proportional mean). If we let *s* denote the geometric mean of *r* and *t*, then it holds that

$$r : s = s : t \text{ or } s^2 = r \cdot t.$$

When the four points *ABPQ* divide each other harmonically, the midpoint *M* of *AB* leads directly to a geometric mean (the same is true of the midpoint of *PQ*). Namely, it holds that

$$MQ : MB = MB : MP.$$

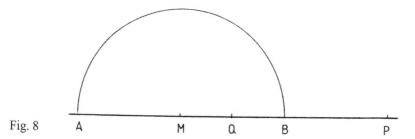

Fig. 8   A   M   Q   B   P

If one sets the radius of the circle, the length of AB, equal to 1, then the connection appears between the interior and the exterior the relationship between Q and P through reciprocals. If the length of MP is denoted by x, and that of MQ by y, then

$$y = \frac{1}{x}.$$

The relationship between the two formulas

$$m = \frac{1}{2}(a+b) \qquad \text{and} \qquad \frac{1}{m} = \frac{1}{2}\left(\frac{1}{a} + \frac{1}{b}\right)$$

for the arithmetic and harmonic means appears here again.

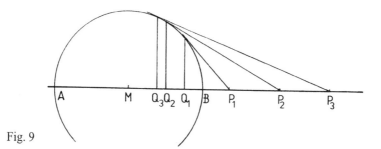

Fig. 9

Let P_2 denote the midpoint of the segment P_1P_3. Let Q_i denote the corresponding points obtained by reflecting P_i through the circle (so that ABP_iQ_i lie in harmonic position). Then MQ_2 is the harmonic mean of MQ_1 and MQ_3.

The transition from harmonic mean to geometric mean holds generally: namely, from $m = \frac{2ab}{a+b}$ it follows that

$$\left(\frac{m}{2}\right)^2 = \left(a - \frac{m}{2}\right) \cdot \left(b - \frac{m}{2}\right).$$

So $\frac{m}{2}$ is therefore the geometric mean of

$$\left(a - \frac{m}{2}\right) \quad \text{and} \quad \left(b - \frac{m}{2}\right).$$

This geometric mean appears in many different ways, particularly with respect to circles.

For any two intersecting chords in a circle, it holds that

$$a_1 \cdot a_2 = b_1 \cdot b_2.$$

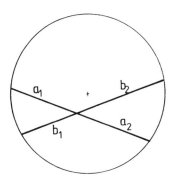

Fig. 10

If one chord is bisected by another, so that, for example of $a_1 = a_2$, then it holds that

$$a_1^2 = b_1 \cdot b_2 \quad \text{or} \quad \frac{b_1}{a_1} = \frac{a_1}{b_2}.$$

Then a_1 is the geometric mean of b_1 and b_2. If the two chords are perpendicular as well, then one obtains the theorem:

$$\frac{p}{h} = \frac{h}{q} \quad \text{or} \quad h^2 = p \cdot q.$$

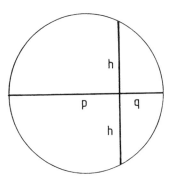

Fig. 11

For two arbitrary secants, we have the relationship $a_1 \cdot a_2 = b_1 \cdot b_2$, where $a_1 = A_1P$, $a_2 = A_2P$, $b_1 = B_1P$ and $b_2 = B_2P$.

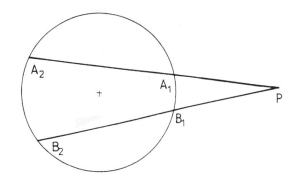

Fig. 12

If $A_1 = A_2$, then the one secant becomes a tangent t and we have the corresponding secant-tangent relationship:

$$t^2 = s_1 \cdot s_2 \quad \text{or} \quad \frac{s_1}{t} = \frac{t}{s_2}$$

So t is therefore the geometric mean of s_1 and s_2, where $PT = s_1$, $PQ = s_2$.

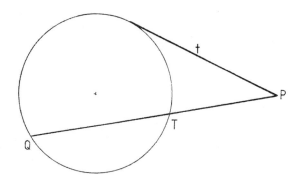

Fig. 13

The above results can brought together in view of the following.

Let P be an arbitrary point outside the circle, let t be a tangent from P to the circle, and let P_1 be the base point of the perpendicular dropped from the point of tangency B to the line PM. The line $S_1 S_2$ is an arbitrary secant through P that will be reflected across the line PM.

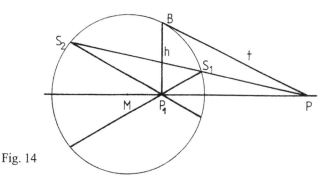

Fig. 14

Let $s_1 = PS_1$, $s_2 = PS_2$, $l_1 = P_1S_1$, and $l_2 = P_1S_2$. For these lengths, then, it holds that

$$l_1 : s_1 = h : t = l_2 : s_2.$$

This holds because the circle about M separates the points P_1 and P. One can also write

$$l_1 : h : l_2 = s_1 : t : s_2$$

The role played by the height h in the interior is played by the tangent t in the exterior.

This relationship is especially poignant if the secant S_1S_2 is rotated about the point P; the chord S_1P_1 revolves then accordingly about P_1. For the student it is of great significance to sense these relationships; the soul is, through precisely this experience, both enriched and harmonized.

Between the three above-mentioned mean values, there is a noteworthy relationship: if a and b are two distinct positive real numbers, then the geometric mean m_g will always lie between the arithmetic mean m_a and the harmonic mean m_h of a and b.

$$m_h < m_g < m_a \text{ or}$$

$$0 < b < \frac{2ab}{a+b} < \sqrt{ab} < \frac{a+b}{2} < a$$

if $b < a$.

Furthermore, the geometric mean of m_a and m_h is equal to the geometric mean of a and b, since

$$m_g^2 = m_a \cdot m_h$$

This relationship can be illustrated in the following sketch:

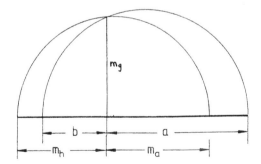

Fig. 15

Thus m_a and m_h lie nearer to m_g than did a and b. If we repeat the process by finding the arithmetic and harmonic mean of m_a and m_h, then we obtain values that are even closer to m_g than were m_a and m_h. This process leads to the conclusion that m_g is in fact the limit of the sequences of successive arithmetic and harmonic means.

With the aid of the geometric mean, the Thales circle can be inverted to form a centrally symmetric hyperbola: h is the geometric mean between AQ and QB. Accordingly, h' is the geometric mean between AP and PB. The points A, B and Q, P lie in harmonic position. It holds that $PC = PC'$, and C' is the intersection of AC and BC'', where C'' is the reflection of C across the line AB.

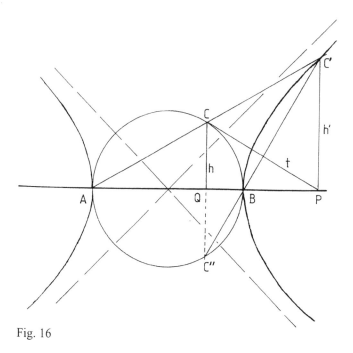

Fig. 16

If h is replaced by the arithmetic mean of AQ and QB, then C will lie on a parallel to AB. If h is replaced by the harmonic mean of AQ and QB, then C will lie on a parabola.

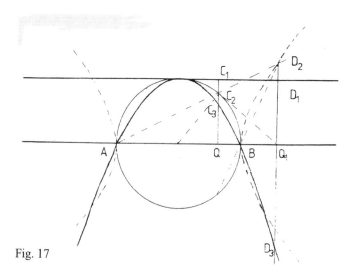

Fig. 17

So QC_1 is the arithmetic mean, QC_2 is the geometric mean, and QC_3 is the harmonic mean of AQ and QB. Accordingly, : Q_1D_1 is the arithmetic mean, Q_1D_2 is the geometric mean, and Q_1D_3 is the harmonic mean of AQ_1 and Q_1B, where Q_1B is (with the exception of the geometric mean) taken to be negative.

Also through the aid of the geometric mean, we can recognize the parabola:
Let h be the geometric mean of a and b. Letting a increase (the point A remains fixed), and holding b constant, the point C will trace out a parabola.

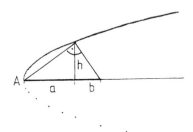

Fig. 18

The parabola appears here as the curve that balances out the difference between a and b, so that: $a : h = h : b$, or $h^2 = ab$. Alternatively, in terms of area, the parabola transforms the rectangle ab into the square h^2. The essence of the parabola lies in the way changes in a are related to changes in h. Replacing h by the arithmetic mean of a and b, one obtains the construction of a line; replacing h by the harmonic mean, one obtains a centrally symmetric hyperbola.

The construction of these three means leads to the corresponding sequences:

In an *arithmetic sequence*, every term is the arithmetic mean of its two neighboring terms:

$$a_n = \frac{1}{2}(a_{n-1} + a_{n+1}) \text{ or}$$

$$a_{n+1} - a_n = a_n - a_{n-1}.$$

Therefore the difference between consecutive terms is constant. Thus it holds that

$$a_n = a_0 + n(a_1 - a_0) \qquad a_{n+1} = a_n + (a_1 - a_0)$$

These three equations also hold for a geometric sequence – one simply needs to increase each operation one level, so to speak.

In a *geometric sequence*, every term is the geometric mean of its two neighboring terms:

$$a_n = \sqrt{a_{n+1} \cdot a_{n-1}}$$
$$\frac{a_{n+1}}{a_n} = \frac{a_n}{a_{n-1}}$$
$$a_n = a_0 \cdot \left(\frac{a_1}{a_0}\right)^n \qquad a_{n+1} = a_n \cdot \frac{a_1}{a_0}.$$

In a *harmonic sequence*, every term is the harmonic mean of its two neighboring terms:

$$\frac{1}{a_n} = \frac{1}{2}\left(\frac{1}{a_{n+1}} + \frac{1}{a_{n-1}}\right) \quad \text{or} \quad \frac{1}{a_{n+1}} - \frac{1}{a_n} = \frac{1}{a_n} - \frac{1}{a_{n-1}}$$

and thus also

$$\frac{1}{a_n} = \frac{1}{a_0} + n\left(\frac{1}{a_1} - \frac{1}{a_0}\right) \qquad \frac{1}{a_{n+1}} = \frac{1}{a_n} + \left(\frac{1}{a_1} - \frac{1}{a_0}\right)$$

or

$$a_n = \frac{a_1 \cdot a_0}{a_1 + n(a_0 - a_1)} \qquad a_{n+1} = \frac{a_n}{1 + a_n\left(\frac{1}{a_1} - \frac{1}{a_0}\right)}.$$

These sequences therefore have the general form:

$$a_n = \frac{c}{a + b \cdot n}.$$

The terms of a harmonic sequence are thus reciprocals of the elements of an arithmetic sequence.

For an arithmetic sequence, $a_{n+1} = a_n + c$;

for a geometric sequence, $a_{n+1} = a_n \cdot c$;

for a harmonic sequence, $a_{n+1} = \frac{a_n}{1 + a_n \cdot c}$.

These three expressions can be combined to

$$a_{n+1} = \frac{\alpha \cdot a_n + \beta}{\gamma \cdot a_n + \delta} \qquad (^*).$$

While arithmetic sequences generally have no finite limit, and harmonic sequences have a limit of zero, geometric sequences have two possible limits: zero and infinity.

The sequence $(^*)$ above generally has, by contrast, two finite limit points u and v, that are of particular significance for the sequence. This is illustrated in the following two examples:

Let

$$a_0 = \frac{1}{2} \quad \text{and} \quad a_{n+1} = \frac{2a_n}{1 + a_n}.$$

One then obtains the sequence

$$a_n = \frac{2^n}{1 + 2^n}.$$

The limit points are $u = 1$ (for $n \to \infty$) and $v = 0$ (for $n \to -\infty$). Furthermore,

$$\frac{u - a_0}{a_0 - v} = \frac{1 - \frac{1}{2}}{\frac{1}{2} - 0} = 1$$

$$\frac{u - a_1}{a_1 - v} = \frac{1 - \frac{2}{3}}{\frac{2}{3} - 0} = \frac{1}{2}$$

$$\frac{u - a_2}{a_2 - v} = \frac{1 - \frac{4}{5}}{\frac{4}{5} - 0} = \frac{1}{4}$$

$$\frac{u - a_3}{a_3 - v} = \frac{1 - \frac{8}{9}}{\frac{8}{9} - 0} = \frac{1}{8}.$$

We see that the ratios of the distances to the limit points form a geometric sequence of ratio $\frac{1}{2}$.

If we let $a_0 = 1$ and $a_{n+1} = \frac{2a_n}{3 + a_n}$, then we obtain the sequence $a_n = \frac{2^n}{2 \cdot 3^n - 2^n}$.

This sequence has the limit points $u = 0$ (for $n \to \infty$) and $v = -1$ (for $n \to -\infty$). Furthermore,

$$\frac{u - a_0}{a_o - v} = \frac{0 - 1}{1 - (-1)} = -\frac{1}{2}$$

$$\frac{u - a_1}{a_1 - v} = \frac{0 - \frac{1}{2}}{\frac{1}{2} - (-1)} = -\frac{1}{3}$$

$$\frac{u - a_2}{a_2 - v} = \frac{0 - \frac{2}{7}}{\frac{2}{7} - (-1)} = -\frac{2}{9}$$

$$\frac{u - a_3}{a_3 - v} = \frac{0 - \frac{4}{23}}{\frac{4}{23} - (-1)} = -\frac{4}{27}.$$

We see that the ratios of the distances to the limit points form a geometric sequence of ratio $\frac{2}{3}$.

The self-orientation toward two quantities and the increasing pattern of ratios affords students the opportunity to develop special qualities in themselves.

The above discussion has shown what a central role is played by the geometric mean. Multiplication appears therein to be more robust than addition. It makes sense, then, that in ancient times the number one was viewed as the center of the numerical realm, a perception that the following diagram also portrays:

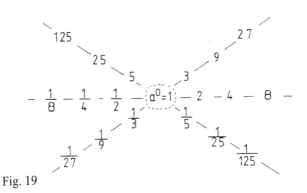

Fig. 19

Every number a, when raised to the zero power, is one ($a \neq 0$). Before a number develops its own character, it is one. Out of the number one, all numbers are created.

This scheme is formed by "reflection" through the number one – one could even say that the numbers are "unified" in the number one, since one is the multiplicative "unit". From a certain point of view, the symmetry about zero in the realm of addition is being carried over to multiplication. For example, the characterization of 4 as a power of 2, as in $4 = 2^2$, or 8 as 2^3, can be broadened to

$$\frac{1}{4} = 2^{-2}, \frac{1}{8} = 2^{-3} \text{ and } 2^{-1} = \frac{1}{2}, 2^0 = 1.$$

One can obtain a refinement of an arithmetic sequence by taking the arithmetic mean of consecutive terms. Accordingly, one can obtain a refinement of the sequence of powers a^n (a geometric sequence) through a "multiplicative mean", that is, through the use of the geometric mean: The sequence

$$\begin{array}{ccccccc} 1 & & 4 & & 16 & & 64... \quad \text{can be refined to} \\ 1 & 2 & 4 & 8 & 16 & 32 & 64... \end{array}$$

since $1 : 2 = 2 : 4, 4 : 8 = 8 : 16$, etc. This leads to the realization that

$$4^{\frac{1}{2}} = 2, \quad 4^{\frac{3}{2}} = 8, \quad 4^{\frac{5}{2}} = 32 \quad \text{etc.}$$

Because these considerations could also be applied to other perfect squares, we realize that

$$a^{\frac{1}{2}} = \sqrt{a}, \quad a^{\frac{3}{2}} = \sqrt{a^3}, \quad a^{\frac{m}{2}} = \sqrt{a^m}.$$

A refinement of the sequence of the powers of 8:

$$\begin{array}{cccccccccc} 8^0 & & & & 8^1 & & & 8^2 & & 8^3 & ... \\ 1 & & & & 8 & & & 64 & & 512 & ... \\ 1 & 2 & 4 & 8 & 16 & 32 & 64 & 128 & 256 & 512 & ... \end{array}$$

then leads to $8^{\frac{1}{3}} = 2, 8^{\frac{2}{3}} = 4, 8^{\frac{4}{3}} = 16$ etc.
In this way, the ratio $1 : 8$ is divided multiplicatively into three equal parts, as $1 : 2 = 2 : 4 = 4 : 8$. Because these considerations could also be applied to other perfect cubes, we realize that

$$a^{\frac{1}{3}} = \sqrt[3]{a}, \quad a^{\frac{2}{3}} = \sqrt[3]{a^2}, \quad a^{\frac{m}{3}} = \sqrt[3]{a^m}$$

and then, in general, that

$$a^{\frac{m}{n}} = \sqrt[n]{a^m}.$$

Because this application is derived more from a rhythmic element, it allows even the weaker students a chance to develop a familiarity with these new concepts. A strict logical development could follow if so desired.

The *inverses* of the operations addition and multiplication lead to an expansion of the concept of number – to negative numbers and fractions. In both cases the question arose historically as to whether such extensions should be considered 'numbers'. It is a matter of reifying a process, where the resulting concepts are manipulated in familiar ways through analogy with the natural numbers. Such issues also arose– with even greater significance – when it came to the inverse of exponentiation: does it even make sense to speak of irrational or imaginary numbers? Consider the following example:

The equation $2^3 = 8$ says that 8 is a transformed, an "intensified" 2. Exponents are a measure of the inner relatedness of numbers, they show how one number transforms into another.

The equation $32^{\frac{6}{5}} = 64$ says that 32 and 64 are formed from a common root, from which the 32 and the 64 are 5 and 6 multiplication steps (in this case doublings) away, respectively.

The equation $2^x = 3$ leads to the interesting question of whether there is a common root for 2 and 3. One can equivalently write $2^{\frac{m}{n}} = 3$ or $2^m = 3^n$; but because 2^m is an even number and 3^n is odd, there is no common root in the above sense. That is, this number cannot be a rational number. Every power of 3 lies between two particular powers of 2:

$$2^m < 3^n < 2^{m+1} \text{ or}$$

$$2^{\frac{m}{n}} < 3 \ < 2^{\frac{m+1}{n}}.$$

This implies – since m can be arbitrarily large – that the powers $2^{\frac{m}{n}}$ are dense, so that 3 can be approached arbitrarily close from above and below. So we can write, for example:

$$2^1 < 2^{\frac{3}{2}} < 2^{\frac{19}{12}} < 2^{\frac{84}{53}} < 3 < 2^{\frac{317}{200}} < 2^{\frac{65}{41}} < 2^{\frac{8}{5}} < 2^2.$$

The exponents are chosen so that:

$$1 < 2 \Leftrightarrow 1 < 2$$

$$\frac{3}{2} < 2 \Leftrightarrow 3 < 4$$

$$\frac{3}{2} < \frac{8}{5} \Leftrightarrow 15 < 16$$

$$\frac{19}{12} < \frac{8}{5} \Leftrightarrow 95 < 96$$

$$\frac{19}{12} < \frac{65}{41} \Leftrightarrow 779 < 780$$

$$\frac{84}{53} < \frac{65}{41} \Leftrightarrow 3444 < 3445$$

$$\frac{84}{53} < \frac{317}{200} \Leftrightarrow 16800 < 16801$$

Because the cross products differ only by 1, the chosen fractions are particularly "efficient". This sequence of fractions can be extended so that a nesting of intervals is formed that, by the completeness axiom, determines a unique real number r for which $2^r = 3$.

This method is both logical and necessary from a modern point of view.

In this scheme (Fig. 20) the powers of 2 are evenly spaced (a logarithmic scale). The number 3 must be placed in such a way that all the powers of 3 (that also must be evenly spaced) are inserted properly between the correct powers of 2. Because the above defined number r is transcendental, all of these "points" 3^n are not constructible.

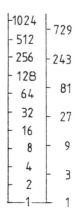

The realm of irrational numbers leads, in this way, to a stronger reliance upon process and less dependence upon visual cues. Visual information aids in clarification but one must also be able to free oneself from it. In mathematics there is an ever present duality: the tendency toward the visible, the fixed, and the tendency toward motion, toward process. The one is concerned with the imagination, the other with the will.

Fig. 20

While addition tends more to the side of imaginative ability, the third-level operations, namely exponentiation with its two inverses radicals and logarithms lead students more toward a conscious use of their will.

To understand that $32^{\frac{6}{5}} = 64$, and that therefore $\log_{32} 64 = \frac{6}{5}$, requires a stronger effort of the will than to understand that $(3+4)+5 = (3+5)+4$.

Addition also has two inverses: one that we might call "quantity comparison" and the other, of course, is subtraction. Consider the example of $3+4 = 7$. Comparing the quantities 3 and 7, a difference of 4 is observed. When I subtract the 4 from the 7, I obtain 3.

From the equation $3 \cdot 2m = 6m$, one can similarly obtain the 3 through a comparison of quantities: the quantity $2m$ is contained three times in the quantity $6m$, that is, I measure the one against the other. On the other hand, if I divide $6m$ into 3 equal parts, I obtain $2m$. In this way, multiplication is also seen to have two inverses.

In the following comparison, however, the differences in these inverses will not be emphasized. It is possible to begin the lesson block on logarithms by transferring calculation rules to a higher level of computation. This can be accomplished through the following comparison.

$$a+b=b+a \qquad \text{vs.} \qquad a \cdot b = b \cdot a$$
$$a+0=a=0+a \qquad\qquad a \cdot 1 = a = 1 \cdot a$$
$$a-a=0 \qquad\qquad a:a=1$$
$$a+(-a)=0 \qquad\qquad a \cdot \frac{1}{a} = 1$$
$$a-b=-(b-a) \qquad\qquad \frac{a}{b} = 1:\frac{b}{a}$$
$$a+(-b)=a-b \qquad\qquad a \cdot \frac{1}{b} = \frac{a}{b}$$
$$a-(-b)=a+b=b-(-a) \qquad\qquad a:\frac{1}{b}=a \cdot b=b:\frac{1}{a}$$
$$(-a)+(-b)=-(a+b) \qquad\qquad \frac{1}{a} \cdot \frac{1}{b} = \frac{1}{a \cdot b}$$

The distributive law also can be carried over:

$$ac+bc=(a+b)c \qquad\qquad a^c \cdot b^c = (a \cdot b)^c$$
$$ac-bc=(a-b)c \qquad\qquad a^c : b^c = (a:c)^c$$

Through examples it will be observed, however, that the following four laws – the four laws of exponents – cannot be quite so directly translated.

$$ab + ac = a(b + c) \qquad \text{vs.} \qquad a^b \cdot a^c = a^{b+c}$$

$$ab - ac = a(b - c) \qquad\qquad a^b : a^c = a^{b-c}$$

$$(a \cdot b)c = a(bc) \qquad\qquad \left(a^b\right)^c = a^{bc}$$

$$(a \cdot b) : c = a \cdot (b : c) \qquad\qquad \sqrt[c]{a^b} = a^{b:c}$$

Notice that in the exponents, the level of operation is not increased – that is the essential characteristic of logarithmic calculations.

After the concept of logarithms is developed, a number of further topics can be explored. Characteristically, one observes that through the two inverses of exponentiation, where it is generally the case that $a^b \neq b^a$, there are multiple possibilities for translation of the rules. Several examples are given in the table on page 29.

The logarithmic spiral combines, in a harmonic way, the arithmetic mean with the geometric mean; an arithmetic mean in the angle corresponds to a geometric mean in the radius. As the angles proceed through an arithmetic sequence, the corresponding radii run through a geometric sequence. In the sketch of the spiral (Fig. 21), an angular increase of $30°$ always corresponds to an increase in the radius by a factor of $\sqrt{3}$.

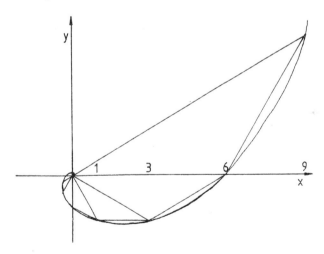

Fig. 21

The spiral is drawn in such a way that it passes through the point $(6, 0)$. If we project the indicated points onto the x-axis, then we obtain the sequence:

$$a_0 = 0; \quad a_1 = 1; \quad a_2 = 3; \quad a_3 = 6; \quad a_4 = 9; \quad a_5 = 9; \quad a_6 = 0; \ \dots$$

and generally that: $a_{n+2} = 3a_{n+1} - 3a_n$. The terms of this sequence grow in accordance with this rule, and it holds that $a_{n+6} = (-27) \cdot a_m$.

From this it follows that the ratios display a 6-step repeating pattern. In other words, if we define $x_n = \frac{a_{n+1}}{a_n}$, then it must hold that $x_{n+6} = x_n$. We have that

$$x_0 = \infty; \; x_1 = 3; \; x_2 = 2; \; x_3 = 1,5; \; x_4 = 1; \; x_5 = 0$$

Joining the point $A\left(\frac{3}{2} \mid \frac{\sqrt{3}}{2}\right)$ with these points on the x-axis, one obtains a constant angle of $30°$. This circling nature of the spiral, that has been projected in the line, has appeared in the sequence of ratios with remarkable purity.

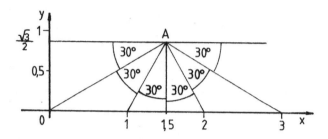

Fig. 22

It can be a special experience for the student to discover the logarithmic spiral in natural forms – for example, in the nautilus shell. In such observations, calculation and measurement agree to an astonishing degree. We discover that that which a human develops in his innermost being is intimately connected with what is formed externally in accordance with the laws of nature.

A student similarly experiences – in trigonometry – the way in which a circular measure, the measure that applies to the cosmos, is closely related to the earthly longitudes. Even here, the student discovers again how laws that are developed through his thought are applicable to the external world.

I	II	III
$(a+b)-b=a=(a-b)+b$ $(a+b)-a=b=a+(b-a)$	$\dfrac{a\cdot b}{b}=a=\dfrac{a}{b}\cdot b \quad \dfrac{a\cdot b}{a}=b=a\cdot\dfrac{b}{a}$	$\sqrt[b]{a^b}=a=(\sqrt[b]{a})^b$ $\log_a a^b=b=a^{\log_a b}$
$(a-b)+c=(a+c)-b=a-(b-c)$	$\dfrac{a}{b}\cdot c=\dfrac{ac}{b}=a:\dfrac{b}{c}$	$(\sqrt[b]{a})^c=\sqrt[b]{a^c}=\sqrt[\frac{b}{c}]{a}$ $(\log_b a)\cdot c=\log_b(a^c)=\log_{\sqrt[c]{b}}a$
$(a-b)-c=(a-c)-b=a-(b+c)$	$(a:b):c=(a:c):b=a:(bc)$	$\sqrt[c]{\sqrt[b]{a}}=\sqrt[b]{\sqrt[c]{a}}=\sqrt[bc]{a}$ $(\log_b a):c=\log_b\sqrt[c]{a}=\log_{b^c}a$
$(a-b)+(b-c)=a-c$	$\dfrac{a}{b}\cdot\dfrac{b}{c}=\dfrac{a}{c}$	$\log_b a\cdot\log_c b=\log_c a$ $(\sqrt[b]{a})^{\frac{b}{c}}=\sqrt[c]{a}$
$(a+c)-(b+c)=a-b$	$\dfrac{ac}{bc}=\dfrac{a}{b}$	$\log_{bc}(a^c)=\log_b a \qquad \sqrt[bc]{a^c}=\sqrt[b]{a}$
$(a-c)-(b-c)=a-b$	$\dfrac{a}{c}:\dfrac{b}{c}=\dfrac{a}{b}$	$\log_c a:\log_c b=\log_b a$ $\log_{\sqrt[c]{b}}\sqrt[c]{a}=\log_b a$ $\sqrt[\frac{b}{\sqrt[c]{b}}]{\sqrt[c]{a}}=\sqrt[b]{a}$
$\dfrac{a}{c}+\dfrac{b}{c}=\dfrac{a+b}{c} \quad \dfrac{a}{c}-\dfrac{b}{c}=\dfrac{a-b}{c}$	$\sqrt[c]{a}\cdot\sqrt[c]{b}=\sqrt[c]{ab} \quad \sqrt[c]{a}:\sqrt[c]{b}=\sqrt[c]{a:b}$	$\log_c a+\log_c b=\log_c(ab)$ $\log_c a-\log_c b=\log_c(a:b)$
$(-a):b=-\dfrac{a}{b}=a:(-b)$ $(-a):(-b)=a:b$	$\sqrt[b]{\dfrac{1}{a}}=\dfrac{1}{\sqrt[b]{a}}=\sqrt[-b]{a} \quad \sqrt[-b]{\dfrac{1}{a}}=\sqrt[b]{a}$	$\log_b\dfrac{1}{a}=-\log_b a$ $\log_{\frac{1}{b}}a=\log_b a$

Introduction to Sine and Tangent

Uwe Hansen

Trigonometry arises from the question: how do curves relate to straight lines? This relationship can be studied in a simple case: suppose a line *g* meets a circle at a point of tangency *B*, and is rotated about *B* through a certain angle α, so that a chord of length *s* is formed.

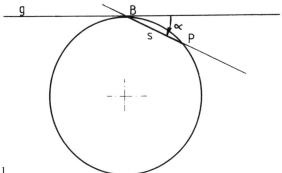

Fig. 1

The length of the chord changes. As α increases, the chord becomes longer at first, until an angle of $\alpha = 90°$ is reached. At this point, the chord has become the diameter of the circle. When $\alpha = 180°$ the chord once again has length zero, as it did when $\alpha = 0°$.

We consider a number of special cases:

1. Case: $\underline{\alpha = 30°}$
In this case, the subtended angle is 60°. An equilateral triangle is formed. The chord is equal in length to the radius, so it forms the side of a regular hexagon: $s = r$.

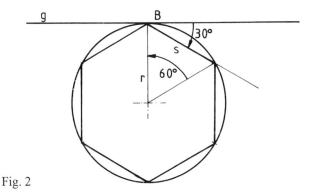

Fig. 2

2. Case: $\alpha = 45°$

In this case, the subtended angle is 90°. The chord is the side of a square inscribed in the circle. It holds that:

$$s^2 = r^2 + r^2 \quad \text{(Pythagorean Theorem)}$$
$$s^2 = 2r^2$$
$$s = r \cdot \sqrt{2}.$$

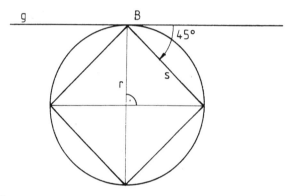

Fig. 3

3. Case: $\alpha = 60°$

In this case, the subtended angle is 120°. The chord is the side of an equilateral triangle inscribed in the circle.

$$s^2 + r^2 = (2r)^2 \quad \text{(PythagoreanTheorem)}$$
$$s^2 + r^2 = 4r^2$$
$$s^2 = 3r^2$$
$$s = r \cdot \sqrt{3}.$$

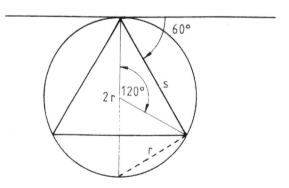

Fig. 4

Overview:

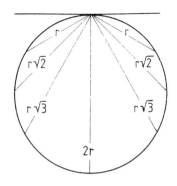

Angle	Chord length	
$\alpha = 0°$	$s = 0$	$= r \cdot \sqrt{0}$
$\alpha = 30°$	$s = r$	$= r \cdot \sqrt{1}$
$\alpha = 45°$	$s = r\sqrt{2}$	$= r \cdot \sqrt{2}$
$\alpha = 60°$	$s = r\sqrt{3}$	$= r \cdot \sqrt{3}$
$\alpha = 90°$	$s = 2r$	$= r \cdot \sqrt{4}$

Fig. 5

The following holds: the chords corresponding to angles α and $180° - \alpha$ have the same length. Moreover, all of the peripheral angles that lie on one side of a chord s must be equal to one another. Peripheral angles on opposite sides of a chord must sum to 180°. $\alpha + \beta = 180°$.

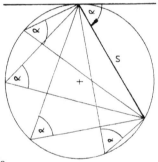

Fig. 6a

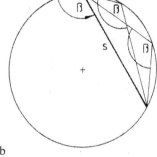

Fig. 6b

The peripheral angles are equal to the corresponding chord-tangent angles. The central angle is twice as large as the smaller of the two peripheral angles (Fig. 7).

All chords that have a peripheral angle of α to any point on the circle must have the same length (Fig. 8).

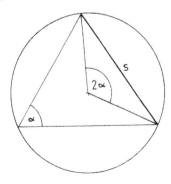

Fig. 7

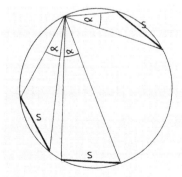

Fig. 8

This leads to the following definition:

The sine of an angle α is the ratio of the chord length s to the diameter of the circle, where the chord corresponds to a peripheral angle of α :

$$\sin\alpha = \frac{\text{chord with peripheral angle } \alpha}{\text{diameter}}$$

$$= \frac{s}{2r}$$

In particular, it holds that: $\sin\alpha = \sin(180° - \alpha)$.

This definition has the advantage that even for angles α between $90°$ and $180°$ the value of sine is immediately explained – the usual treatment of these angles is often too obscure for students.

We can expand the table above to:

Peripheral-angle	Chord-length	$\frac{\text{Chord length}}{\text{Diameter}} = \frac{s}{2r}$	Abbreviation
$\alpha = 0°$	0	$\frac{0}{2r} = 0$	$\sin 0° = 0$
$\alpha = 30°$	r	$\frac{r}{2r} = \frac{1}{2}$	$\sin 30° = \frac{1}{2}$
$\alpha = 45°$	$r\sqrt{2}$	$\frac{r\sqrt{2}}{2r} = \frac{1}{2}\sqrt{2}$	$\sin 45° = \frac{1}{2}\sqrt{2}$
$\alpha = 60°$	$r\sqrt{3}$	$\frac{r\sqrt{3}}{2r} = \frac{1}{2}\sqrt{3}$	$\sin 60° = \frac{1}{2}\sqrt{3}$
$\alpha = 90°$	$2r$	$\frac{2r}{2r} = 1$	$\sin 90° = 1$
$\alpha = 120°$	$r\sqrt{3}$	$\frac{r\sqrt{3}}{2r} = \frac{1}{2}\sqrt{3}$	$\sin 120° = \frac{1}{2}\sqrt{3}$
$\alpha = 135°$	$r\sqrt{2}$	$\frac{r\sqrt{2}}{2r} = \frac{1}{2}\sqrt{2}$	$\sin 135° = \frac{1}{2}\sqrt{2}$
$\alpha = 150°$	r	$\frac{r}{2r} = \frac{1}{2}$	$\sin 150° = \frac{1}{2}$
$\alpha = 180°$	0	$\frac{0}{2r} = 0$	$\sin 180° = 0$

For angles $\alpha > 180°$ this approach leads us to the right idea:

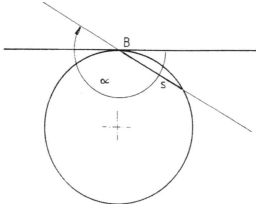

Fig. 9

Suppose that $\alpha = 210°$. It must hold that $\sin 210° = -\frac{1}{2}$, because the chord is now measured in the opposite direction.

The Law of Sines is a direct consequence of our choice of definition:

$$\sin \alpha = \frac{a}{2r}$$
$$\sin \beta = \frac{b}{2r}$$
$$\sin \gamma = \frac{c}{2r},$$

therefore

$$2r = \frac{a}{\sin \alpha} = \frac{b}{\sin \beta} = \frac{c}{\sin \gamma}.$$

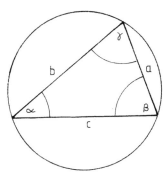

Fig. 10

Here, the sides of the triangle are the chords, and the angles of the triangle are the corresponding peripheral angles in the circle circumscribed about the triangle.

With the help of these newly introduced concepts, a wide variety of exercises can be posed.

A few examples: below, the triangle or quadrilateral is to be constructed and its perimeter is to be computed. The given angles are chord-tangent angles (Figs. 11 to 13). The results are: $U_{11} = 14.2\,\text{cm}$; $U_{12} = 16.68\,\text{cm}$; $U_{13} = 11.2\,\text{cm}$

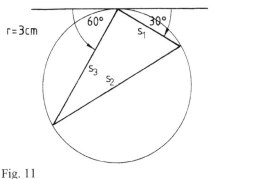

Fig. 11

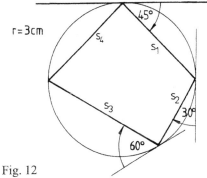

Fig. 12

A triangle is uniquely determined when two of its angles and the circumradius are known. The sides and the perimeter of the triangle can then be calculated.

35

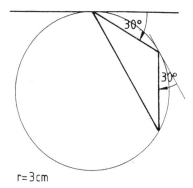

Fig. 13   r = 3 cm

For example: $r = 3$ cm, $\alpha = 30°$, $\beta = 60°$. It follows that $a = 3$ cm, $b = 3\sqrt{3}$ cm, $c = 6$ cm, $U = 14.2$ cm.
Or: $\alpha = 15°$, $\beta = 45°$, $r = 3$ cm.

Because $\sin 15° = \frac{1}{2}\sqrt{2-\sqrt{3}} = 0.2588$, it follows that $a = 1.55$ cm, $b = 4.24$ cm, $c = 5.2$ cm and $U = 10.99$ cm. For the construction it is sensible to use the central angle.

Suppose one knows the circumradius of a triangle, one side, and one angle that is not opposite this side. Then the solution is unique if the given angle is between the two peripheral angles of the given side. For example, if $r = 3$ cm, $b = 3\sqrt{3}$ cm, then there are two solutions whenever $\alpha < 60°$. If $60° < \alpha < 120°$, then there is exactly one solution. But if $\alpha > 120°$, then there is no solution, because the sum of the angles in a triangle cannot exceed $180°$.

Suppose one knows the circumradius of a triangle and two sides. Then there are two solutions that are distinct whenever the two sides are distinct and both are shorter than the diameter of the circle. If the circumradius is not known, then the triangles can be calculated with the help of the Law of Sines whenever a side and its corresponding angle is given. Otherwise one can use the Law of Cosines (cf. the Bernhard article).

It is reasonable to define cosine as

$$\cos \alpha = \sin(90° + \alpha)$$

Because $\sin \alpha = \sin(180° - \alpha)$ it also follows that

$$\begin{aligned}
\cos \alpha &= \sin(90° + \alpha) \\
&= \sin(180° - (90° + \alpha)) \\
&= \sin(90° - \alpha)
\end{aligned}$$

If we treat the diameter as unity and we let α vary, then it is easy to observe the complementary relationship between $\sin \alpha$ and $\cos \alpha$. In particular:

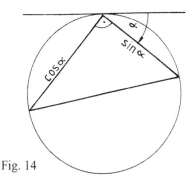

$$\cos 0° = 1$$
$$\cos 30° = \frac{1}{2}\sqrt{3}$$
$$\cos 45° = \frac{1}{2}\sqrt{2}$$
$$\cos 60° = \frac{1}{2}$$
$$\cos 90° = 0$$

and

$$\sin^2 \alpha + \cos^2 \alpha = 1$$

Fig. 14

For right triangles we have the following simplification: when the leg from α becomes a diameter of the circle, then a right triangle is formed (Thales circle). The chord becomes the leg opposite α, and the diameter is the hypotenuse.

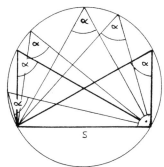

Fig. 15

For right triangles, then, it holds that

$$\sin \alpha = \frac{\text{side opposite } \alpha}{\text{hypotenuse}}$$

Experience shows that it is not difficult for students to use both definitions. Note, also, that from the first (general) definition, it is possible to derive a corresponding definition of tangent. What the chord is for the interior of the circle, the tangent is for the exterior.

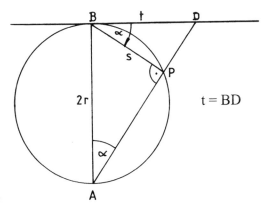

Fig. 16

37

As α increases, the point P traverses the circle; the line AP cuts a segment t from the tangent that corresponds to the chord s. Similar to the definition of sine, we could express:

$$\tan\alpha = \frac{\text{tangential segment for angle } \alpha}{\text{diameter}} = \frac{t}{2r}$$

At B there appears a right angle, so that:

$$\tan\alpha = \frac{\text{opposite leg from } \alpha}{\text{adjacent leg to } \alpha}$$

As in the case of sine, a number of values of tangent can be calculated directly from the diagram:

1. Case: $\underline{a = 45°}$

The triangle ABD is isosceles, so $t = 2r$ and $\tan 45° = 1$

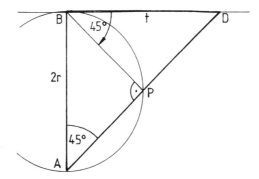

Fig. 17

2. Case: $\underline{a = 60°}$

Because $\sin 30° = \frac{1}{2}$, we have $AD = 2d$. Then

$$t^2 = (2d)^2 - d^2 = 3d^2$$
$$t = d\sqrt{3}$$

and

$$\tan 60° = \frac{t}{d} = \frac{d\sqrt{3}}{d} = \sqrt{3}.$$

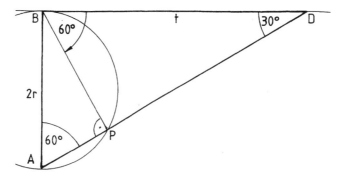

Fig. 18

From the triangle (Fig. 18) we also deduce that

$$\tan 30° = \frac{1}{\sqrt{3}}$$

As the angle α approaches the value $\alpha = 90°$, the segment BD becomes infinitely long. Therefore $\tan 90° = \infty$.

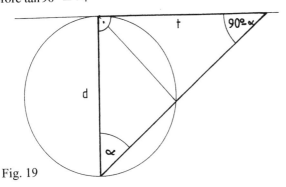

$$\tan 0° = 0$$
$$\tan 30° = \frac{1}{\sqrt{3}}$$
$$\tan 45° = 1$$
$$\tan 60° = \sqrt{3}$$
$$\tan 90° = \infty$$

Fig. 19

It holds that

$$\tan \alpha \cdot \tan(90° - \alpha) = \frac{t}{d} \cdot \frac{d}{t} = 1$$

For $\alpha = 135°$ the leg AP cuts the tangent line on the other side. One sees that $\tan 135° = -1$. In general it holds that:

$$\tan(180° - \alpha) = -\tan \alpha$$

The polarity of sine and tangent – the sine relates to the chord as the tangent does to the tangent line – can also be seen in the calculation of the perimeter of the inscribed or circumscribed n-gon:

$$s_n = 2r \cdot \sin \frac{180°}{n} \qquad t_n = 2r \cdot \tan \frac{180°}{n}$$

Deriving polarities, such as internal-external or curved-straight, is an important landmark for the maturing student.

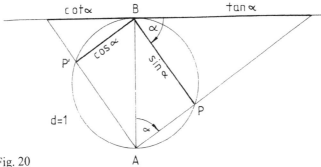

Fig. 20

If we define cotangent by $\cot = \tan(90° - \alpha)$, then Fig. 20 shows the relationship between the 4 angle functions, where the cotangent axis runs in the direction opposite to that of the tangent.

Extensions:

The sine of an angle can also be introduced by way of the Thales circle, through the question: In what relationship does the diameter of the circle decrease when the angle $90°$ changes to angle α? In this way we can understand the statement $\sin 30° = \frac{1}{2}$: As the $90°$-angle decreases to $30°$, the diameter decreases by one half.

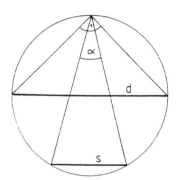

Fig. 21

Here again the relationship of the chord to the diameter is being used. By the theorem of peripheral angles, this definition extends to triangles that are not isosceles.

Independently of sine, the cosine can be introduced as the projection of one ray of an angle onto the other. So one could, for example, define it through the division of the hypotenuse of a right triangle:

$$\cos \alpha = \frac{p}{b} \qquad \cos \beta = \frac{q}{a}.$$

It then follows immediately that

$$\cos 0° = 1, \quad \cos 60° = \frac{1}{2}, \quad \cos 90° = 0.$$

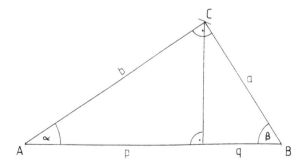

Fig. 22

By the similarity of the triangles

$$\cos\beta = \frac{a}{c} \quad \text{or} \quad a = c \cdot \cos\beta.$$

When c is constant this is the equation of a circle in polar coordinates. Through this, it is clear that we must set:

$$\cos(-\beta) = \cos\beta \quad \text{and} \quad \cos(180° - \beta) = -\cos\beta.$$

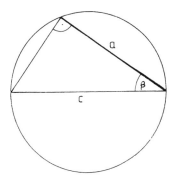

Fig. 23

The tangent of an angle α can also be introduced through the ratio

$$\tan\alpha = \frac{\text{stake length}}{\text{shadow length}} \quad \text{where the angle of the sun is } \alpha$$

This implies $\tan 45° = 1$: when the sun stands at $45°$ the shadow is as long as the stake.

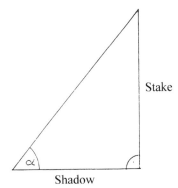

Fig. 24

Stake

Shadow

A few exercises regarding tangent:

1.

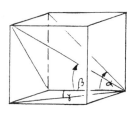

Fig. 25

Determine the angles α, β, γ. The triangles lie in a cube.

Solution:

$\alpha = \gamma = 45°$; $\tan\beta = \sqrt{2}$; $\beta = 54.74°$

2.

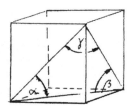

Fig. 26

Determine the angles α, β, γ. The triangles lie in a cube.

Solution:

The triangle is equilateral; $\alpha = \beta = \gamma = 60°$

3.

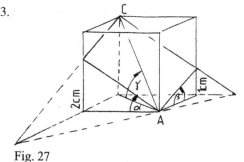

Fig. 27

The edge of the cube has length 3 cm. Determine the angles α, β, γ.

Solution:

$\alpha = 33.69°$, $\beta = 18.43°$, $\gamma = 35.26°$. γ is not the steepest angle of the plane. A ball would not roll from C to A. The maximal angle is $\delta = 36.7°$.

4.

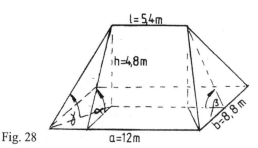

Fig. 28

Determine the angles α, β, γ of the hipped roof.

Solution:

$\alpha = 47.49°$, $\beta = 55.49°$, $\gamma = 41.11°$.

A young man (eye level 1.60 m) observes a young lady (1.75 m tall) on a balcony of height 8 m. Under what angle does the lady appear to the man when he is 20 m from the house?

Solution: the angle amounts to 4.42°.

How close must the man approach to the house in order to maximize the angle?

Solution: the distance is 7.22 m. The maximum angle is 6.91°. One considers a circle in which the lady is a vertical chord and which touches a line parallel to the ground at the eye level of the man.

The Sine Disk

Jürgen Vogt

It is a straightforward matter to take the definitions of the trigonometric functions in terms of chords on a circle, as described in the article from Uwe Hansen, and use them to build a tool from which the values of sine and cosine can be read off through a simple turn. All that is needed are two circular disks that can be turned relative to one another. The common point of rotation is the center M.

On the lower disk (the base), made out of cardboard or sturdy paper, a circle is drawn that passes through the center M, and its tangent at M. Along the outer edge of the disk, angles are marked all around.

The upper, transparent disk (the overlay) has only a cross of two perpendicular axes through M with the corresponding symbols for sine and cosine and marked with a scale. The scale is chosen so that "1" corresponds to the diameter of the first disk. If desired, the special angles could also be marked, such as $\sin 45° = \frac{1}{2}\sqrt{2}$. It is also appropriate to place negative values on each of the other halves of the two axes. A small mark on the outer edge of the transparent disk facilitates the exact alignment of the angles.

From the scale on the horizontal tangent, the values of tangent and cotangent can be read. To do so, a ruler is laid on the lowest point of the circle and the intersection point of the circle and the sine scale. The scale is then read at the point where the ruler crosses the horizontal tangent. The value corresponds to the tangent of the angle. If the ruler is laid on the lowest point of the the the circle and the intersection of the circle with the cosine scale, then the cotangent is given. Care should be taken with the signs of the numbers since sine and cosine use the same scale. So that angles greater than 45° can be easily read, two smaller circles are given, for which the measured values must be multiplied by two or four. A bit less conveniently, but with equal precision, the values of tangent for angles greater than 45° can also be ascertained since their cotangents can be measured and reciprocated.

With the sine disk, it is just as easy to determine the values of sine and cosine for arbitrary angles as it is to accomplish the inverse: from arbitrary values for sine and cosine, we can determine the corresponding angle. The advantage the sine disk has over a table is clear: the student constantly has the derivation of sine before his eyes. Furthermore, the measured values they obtain will not be unnecessarily exact for the purposes of their hand calculations.

The upper disk can be most easily made from an overhead slide or a transparency. For the base disk, a heavy stock paper or cardboard will suffice. Depending on the circumstances, the circle, tangent, angle scale and pair of axes can be traced or photocopied onto the disks if they are not to be drawn by the students themselves. The patterns for both disks are included here, or they can be downloaded from www.lehrerseminar-forschung.de if desired (choose "Lehrmittel- und Büchershop". The disks are meant to be cut out along the dotted lines. A thumbtack works well as a point of rotation: first put a hole through the point M, then bend the end of the tack and secure it in place with a bit of glue. The exactness with which the hole in the center is placed is critical for the precision of the instrument.

Base

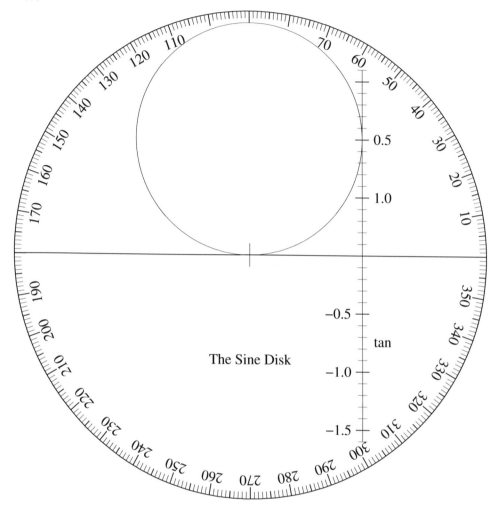

The Sine Disk

Overlay

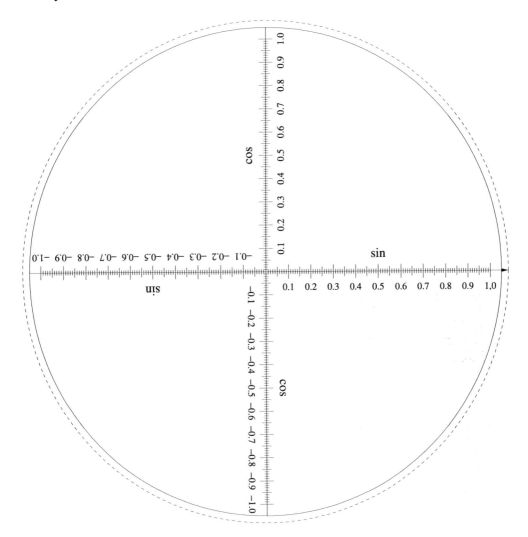

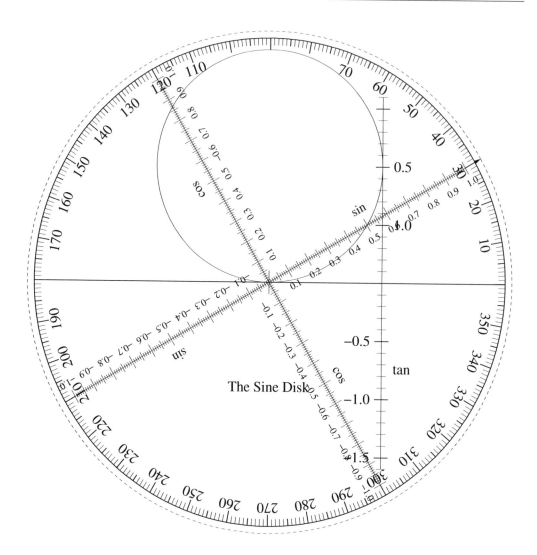

The Sine Disk

Trigonometry in the 10th Grade

Arnold Bernhard

Preliminary Remarks

In this article I have recorded my experiences with trigonometry instruction in the 10th grade as I have gathered it over a span of 25 years at the Rudolf Steiner School in Basel.

It has always been my concern to awaken, as much as possible, the students' own activity. Therefore I have often begun with concrete numerical or constructive exercises which students could solve under their own effort without requiring much support from the teacher. Out of the experiences they gained from these exercises, I was able to develop the necessary general viewpoints. This methodology indeed requires more time than others, but it leads to a solid knowledge and understanding on the part of the students. In writing this piece I have made an effort throughout to ensure that this way of proceeding, the methodology, was visible to the reader. In this respect, the work is rather detailed. Throughout the text, the echoes of the classroom conversation should come through. In this way the work can serve as an example-rich guide through the material for the colleague who has not taught this lesson block often. It is also quite possible to modify the given curriculum in many respects: it could be given different accents and points of emphasis, the sine and cosine curves could be introduced already, and still other additional topics could be included. I have only introduced other topics systematically with 11th graders, and that was with a study of the acoustical phenomenon of a tuning fork. It would be possible, however, to incorporate still other exploration topics.

In producing this piece, I have tried to strike a compromise between perfectionism and efficiency. So, for example, in the drawings I didn't always use instruments. Right angles were not always denoted when it was clear from context that they were meant. Because such texts are intended for internal usage, they need not be absolutely perfect in the details of the presentation. Under these terms, perhaps more of our colleagues will be encouraged to contribute material. It would be nice if such articles would appear from even more of our colleagues, so that a true exchange and mutual stimulation could take place.

In the course presented here, I generally have at my disposal four weeks of main lesson block in the 10th grade. In two weeks, I treat general similarity, similarity of triangles, and the trigonometry of right angled triangles (parts I through V in the present work). For the law of sines (part VI) and the law of cosines (part VII), I spend one week each.

Because my main priority in this presentation was to make a methodology apparent, I have left out some applied exercises that I solved with the students partly in the lesson block and partly in the weekly math lessons that followed. Such exercises can be found in abundance in the exercise collections. Regarding precision in computations, I have generally agreed with the classes upon two decimal places. This level of precision is reasonable for all exercises that are drawn and calculated in centimeters.

I have always viewed 10th grade trigonometry (as well as the algebra in this grade) as the first true introduction to high school mathematics. The students take critical steps forward in this lesson block. If they complete them successfully, then a good foundation is laid for all that lies ahead of them.

I. Central Similarity

Because all of trigonometry is concerned with similarity of triangles, it is fitting first to treat similarity in general. Particularly well-suited to our task is the concept of *central* similarity: we draw any arbitrary polygon (for example a quadrilateral), choose anywhere a center point Z, connect it with the vertices (similarity rays), and slide the sides outward in a parallel manner. A polygon so formed will have the *same* form as the original.

The center can be chosen in the interior, on the boundary, or even outside the figure (see Figures 1 to 4 on the next page). Each figure can also be viewed as a contraction rather than an expansion.

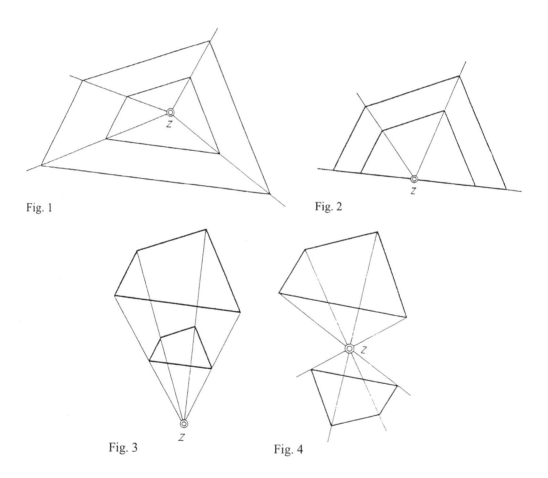

Fig. 1   Fig. 2

Fig. 3   Fig. 4

How does the polygon change if we forego the use of a central point, and simply slide the sides in any arbitrary manner that keeps them parallel to the original sides (Fig. 5)? The two polygons obviously can have different form; they agree naturally still in the angles, but not necessarily in the proportions of the sides.

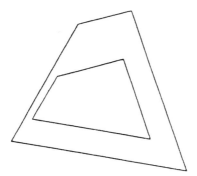

Fig. 5

Does the form remain the same if we slide each of the sides of the polygon *an equal distance –* for example, through the width of a ruler (Fig. 6)?

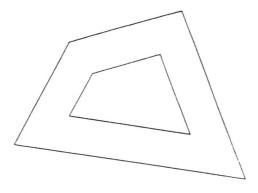

Fig. 6

Even in this figure, the proportions of the sides have changed. So why is the form preserved when the vertices are shifted along rays from a central point? In such an operation there arise many instances of the *intercept theorems*, which ensure that all the sides are expanded or contracted in the *same proportion* (similarity relation); the proportions between the sides then also remain the same. *Key observation*: figures have the same form whenever they agree not only in the *angles*, but also in the *proportions of the sides*. Such figures are said to be similar.

Counterexamples:

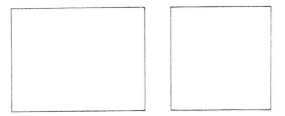

Only equal angles

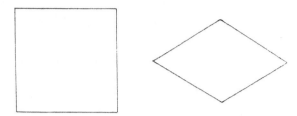

Only equal proportions of sides

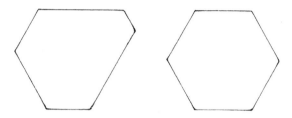

Only equal angles

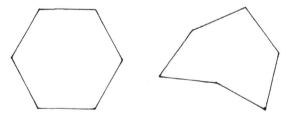

Only equal proportions of sides

Quadrilaterals, pentagons, hexagons ... can therefore satisfy the first of these conditions without satisfying the second, or vice-versa. Drawing exercises for central similarity: enlarge Figures 7 through 9 from the given center Z to double the original size (solutions given in Fig. 10 through 12).

When a circle is centrally expanded or contracted through its center, then it is clear that a circle will result. But what happens if the center point of similarity is *not* taken to be the center of the circle?

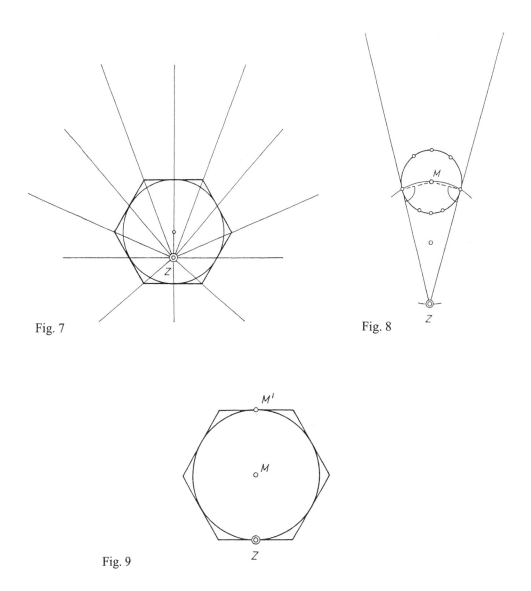

Fig. 7

Fig. 8

Fig. 9

The students will be surprised to learn that the result will always be a circle, no matter where the center point of similarity is chosen. But of course every figure that is similar to a circle must itself be a circle.

In exercises given in Fig. 10 to Fig. 12, the students should clearly imagine how the vertices and sides move through the steps of these constructions: the vertices slide along rays through the center, and the sides are pushed in a parallel manner. If the students can envision these paths of motion as an expansion from a center or as a contraction toward a center, then they should be able to find the solutions to the following written exercises.

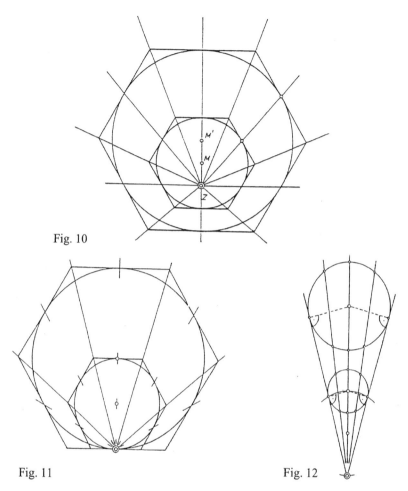

Fig. 10

Fig. 11

Fig. 12

Inscribe a square inside a circle, a semicircle, a circular sector, or a triangle. The number of solutions varies from problem to problem (Fig. 13 to 19).

The solution principle is always the same: first one chooses a square that is too large or too small that is in a well-chosen location, and then one contracts or expands it from a center point.

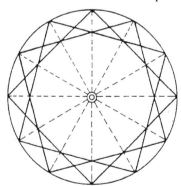

Fig. 13

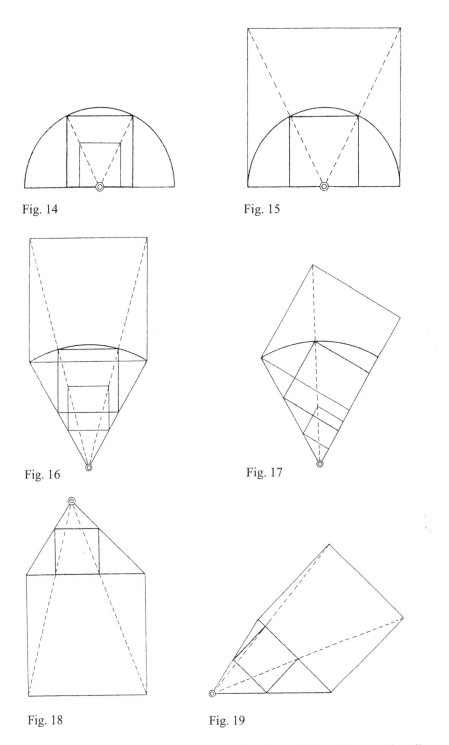

Fig. 14

Fig. 15

Fig. 16

Fig. 17

Fig. 18

Fig. 19

The following exercise is particularly nice: construct the circle which touches two given lines and passes through a given point P (Fig. 20 and 21).

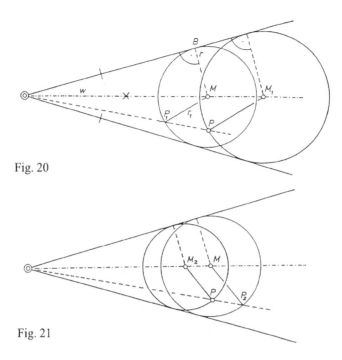

Fig. 20

Fig. 21

A great deal is gained when we can imagine how the central similarity is an expanding or contracting motion that extends from the central point over the entire plane, not only into its farthest reaches – but also arbitrarily close to the center. This motion can be thought of as being fast, slow, or of changing speed. If the motion assumes a constant speed, one that is depicted in regular intervals, then the distances of the vertices from the center at these instants will form geometric sequences; the different vertices share a common ratio (Fig. 22a, b, c).

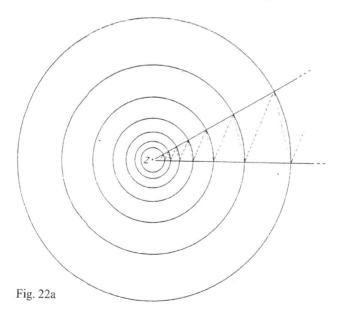

Fig. 22a

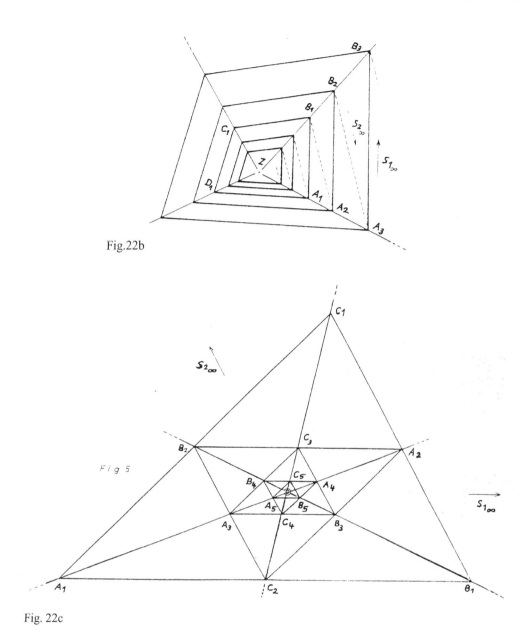

Fig.22b

Fig 5

Fig. 22c

II. The Similarity of Triangles

Recall the drawing experiment that we conducted with quadrilaterals, pentagons, hexagons... etc: to slide the sides in a parallel manner, regardless of whether or not the motion was determined through rays from a central point or not. We now perform this same experiment on triangles. Of course a similar triangle to the original will always result whenever the motion is determined through a central point. But if we instead do not use a central point and just move the sides in some other parallel manner, then we arrive at the surprising observation that the new triangle is indeed always similar to the original triangle (Fig. 23 through 26). If we go back afterwards and connect the corresponding vertices with each other (those with equal angles), then these connecting lines appear magically to coincide at a central point. And indeed, if such a central point were to exist for every parallel displacement of the sides, then it would certainly have to be the case that the new triangle is similar to the original.

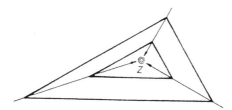

Fig. 23

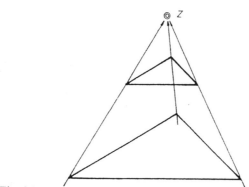

Fig. 24

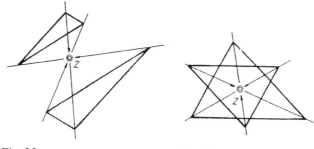

Fig. 25   Fig. 26

It has been my experience that with many 10th grade classes, these drawing experiments have been so convincing that the students did not even demand proof for the existence of the central point. In these cases I simply indicated that there is a general theorem concerning the relative positions of two triangles (the theorem of Desargues), which guarantees the existence of the center of similarity, and which is thoroughly treated in the 11th grade in the context of projective geometry. If a class is not content to wait that long, then the proof for the existence of the central point of similarity can be carried through in the same manner as the proof of the general theorem of Desargues when the existence of one axis is assumed (Fig. 27). One chooses in a parallel plane E' a third triangle with parallel sides and joins the corresponding vertices of the first two triangles. Elementary theorems governing position and incidence of objects in space ensure the existence of the two center points Z_1 and Z_2. The intersection point of the line Z_1Z_2 with the plane E of the first two triangles is the center of similarity. This fact also follows from elementary geometric considerations in the plane.

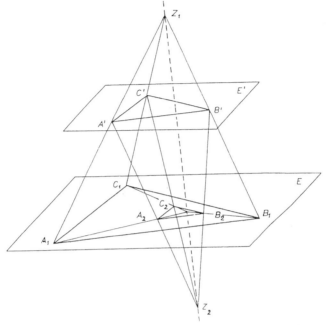

Fig. 27

Through each of the three sides of the triangle $A'B'C'$ in the plane E' and the corresponding parallel sides of each of the two triangles in plane E, there passes a plane. These three planes form the sides of a pyramid: upward there rises a pyramid with apex Z_1; the edges of this pyramid are the connecting lines joining corresponding vertices (A_1A', B_1B', C_1C'). Downward there descends a pyramid with apex Z_2; its edges are the connecting lines $A'A_2$, $B'B_2$ and $C'C_2$.

We complete Figure 27 by adding the connecting line v that joins the two points Z_1 and Z_2 (the dashed line). The line v and the pyramid edges $Z_1A'A_1$ and Z_2A_2A' intersect each other mutually, forming a triangle, and therefore must be coplanar. This plane cuts the plane E in the line A_1A_2, which must also meet v, namely at the intersection point of v with E. From similar considerations it follows that the lines B_1B_2 and C_1C_2 also pass through this point. *This is the center of similarity of the two triangles in plane E.* Therefore the existence of this central point is necessarily determined, and is not a coincidence of the drawings!

This entire discussion shows that the consideration of similarity of triangles is quite different from that of other polygons: whenever triangles agree in their angles, then the proportions of their sides must also agree (and vice-versa). In triangles, the one agreement implies the other;

with quadrilaterals, pentagons, etc., we have seen for ourselves that they may agree in the angles only or in the proportions of the sides only. This is not possible with triangles; either they must agree in both side proportions and angles, or in neither. This fact is the basis of trigonometry.

III. Computations with Side Proportions

Before we introduce the class to the concepts of sine, cosine, tangent, and cotangent, it is worth calculating with side proportions in triangles more generally. This can be achieved through the following exercises:

Draw the triangle with sides $c_1 = 10$ cm, $a_1 = 9$ cm, $b_1 = 8$ cm. Add to this drawing a second, similar triangle with side $c_2 = 8.4$ cm. Measure sides a_2 and b_2 and also calculate their length (Fig. 28).

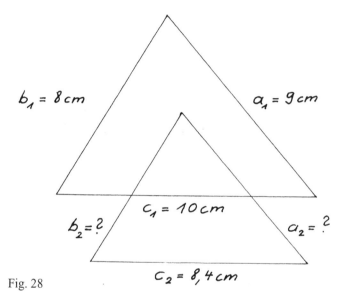

Fig. 28

We draw the side c_2 anywhere parallel to c_1 with the prescribed length and we move the sides a and b parallel as well. We can have some of the students write the measured lengths of a_2 and b_2 on the chalkboard; they will differ slightly between students. But the students will notice: a_2 and b_2 must have very specific lengths. However, with drawing and measuring, they can only approximate the correct value. The exact determination is possible only through computation: the two triangles agree in all three angles, and therefore also in the side proportions.

$$\frac{a_2}{c_2} = \frac{a_1}{c_1} \quad \frac{a_2}{8.4} = \frac{9}{10} \quad a_2 = \frac{9}{10} \cdot 8.4 \quad a_2 = \underline{7.56\,\text{cm}}$$

$$\frac{b_2}{c_2} = \frac{b_1}{c_1} \quad \frac{b_2}{8.4} = \frac{8}{10} \quad b_2 = \frac{8}{10} \cdot 8.4 \quad b_2 = \underline{6.72\,\text{cm}}$$

If we could draw with absolute perfection, then the two sides in question would have exactly these lengths. I believe it is important, however, that we perform both the drawing and the calculation.

The drawing is a perception, while the calculation is, aside from the visible digits, a purely conceptual process. Understanding takes place when we find a conceptual context for a perception. This is the basis of all understanding; it can be exemplified and experienced in precisely such exercises. And it is good to solve many such examples with the class. The second triangle can assume very different positions in relation to the first.

Second example:
$c_1 = 12\,\text{cm}$, $a_1 = 7\,\text{cm}$, $b_1 = 9\,\text{cm}$, $a_2 = 4.3\,\text{cm}$

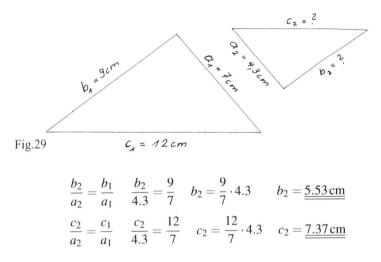

Fig.29

$$\frac{b_2}{a_2} = \frac{b_1}{a_1} \qquad \frac{b_2}{4.3} = \frac{9}{7} \qquad b_2 = \frac{9}{7} \cdot 4.3 \qquad b_2 = \underline{5.53\,\text{cm}}$$

$$\frac{c_2}{a_2} = \frac{c_1}{a_1} \qquad \frac{c_2}{4.3} = \frac{12}{7} \qquad c_2 = \frac{12}{7} \cdot 4.3 \qquad c_2 = \underline{7.37\,\text{cm}}$$

IV. Introduction to the Trigonometric Ratios

Once the students have become accustomed to computing with the side ratios of similar triangles that may be acute or obtuse, then one can begin to consider the special case of right-angled triangles. We can assign students the task of drawing a right-angled triangle with a given angle β, for example, $\beta = 35°$. We make no specification regarding the lengths of the sides; every student can draw the triangle in his own size. Then everyone should calculate the ratios b/c, a/c, b/a, and a/b. Again we have the students report their numbers and we make a table on the chalkboard (Fig. 30).

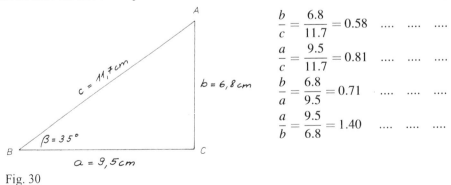

$$\frac{b}{c} = \frac{6.8}{11.7} = 0.58 \quad \dots \quad \dots \quad \dots$$

$$\frac{a}{c} = \frac{9.5}{11.7} = 0.81 \quad \dots \quad \dots \quad \dots$$

$$\frac{b}{a} = \frac{6.8}{9.5} = 0.71 \quad \dots \quad \dots \quad \dots$$

$$\frac{a}{b} = \frac{9.5}{6.8} = 1.40 \quad \dots \quad \dots \quad \dots$$

Fig. 30

The reported values will differ slightly (but only slightly!) from one another, even though all the students drew triangles in their own chosen size. Obviously these ratios are independent of the size of the triangle. We repeat the same experiment with a different angle, say $\beta = 65°$. Again we have the same effect: all the students report approximately the same ratios. The values must apparently be determined by the angle β. Of course! If all the students draw a right triangle with a specific angle β, then all the various triangles in each of their notebooks must agree in all three angles; therefore they are similar and must also agree in the proportions of their sides. – Now one can announce to the class:

In right triangles, these ratios have names:

$$\frac{b}{c} = \text{sine of } \beta \qquad \text{in short:} \qquad \frac{b}{c} = \sin\beta$$

$$\frac{a}{c} = \text{cosine of } \beta \qquad\qquad\qquad \frac{a}{c} = \cos\beta$$

$$\frac{b}{a} = \text{tangent of } \beta \qquad\qquad\qquad \frac{b}{a} = \tan\beta$$

$$\frac{a}{b} = \text{cotangent of } \beta \qquad\qquad\qquad \frac{a}{b} = \cot\beta$$

The students will have heard and read these names before, and they will have wondered what they meant. Now they experience something like "enlightenment": Aha – so the ratios of the sides of a right-angled triangle are what these names stand for! The experience can be almost festive; in any case, it is a pleasant moment. The notions of the adjacent and opposite sides enter into this moment like into a fertile soil. Permanently anchored into this foundation are the following:

$$\text{sine of an angle} = \frac{\text{opposite}}{\text{hypotenuse}} = \frac{\text{O}}{\text{H}}$$

$$\text{cosine of an angle} = \frac{\text{adjacent}}{\text{hypotenuse}} = \frac{\text{A}}{\text{H}}$$

$$\text{tangent of an angle} = \frac{\text{opposite}}{\text{adjacent}} = \frac{\text{O}}{\text{A}}$$

$$\text{cotangent of an angle} = \frac{\text{adjacent}}{\text{opposite}} = \frac{\text{A}}{\text{O}}$$

As teachers, we might know the method by which the particular ratios can be determined exactly. But how much of this we can present to the students depends on the facilities available the students, and upon our skill (and luck) in teaching. In any case, over the course of this lesson block, the students should get some idea of how generations of humanity had to work for centuries on the mathematical and technical developments that led to the highly developed calculation machine that they know as the modern calculator.

Next we introduce the students to the use of the calculator. We simply show them how we enter an angle and then ask it to calculate, say, the sine of this angle. A decimal expression with many digits appears in the display! A glance at our table: yes, the values that we determined using our drawings are nearly matched by the values given by the calculator. Naturally this raises question upon question! How does the calculator do it? How did people figure out how to build such a magic box? Because the students determined the ratios first through their drawings, at least approximately, they have some relationship to the number that appears in the display. It is not so foreign to them, and neither is their calculator. We have to bring the students, over time, into kind of a free relationship with their calculators: it cannot terrify them with the fear of the unknown, nor should it mystify them as a magic box. To reach this goal, many advances must be made in both mathematics and technology.

We conclude this chapter with a comment regarding methodology: there are colleagues who introduce the definitions by way of the unit circle, and then treat the trigonometric ratios as special cases of these periodic functions. This, it could be argued, is perhaps a more economical use of time. However in classes where this choice has been made, I have observed that many students, particularly the weaker ones of course, remain uncertain in their use of trigonometric ratios. Whoever chooses to pursue this route should be aware of this danger and be sure to plan enough time for practicing the use of trigonometric ratios. In the course of study presented here, such practice can be found in the next chapter.

V. Practice with Trigonometric Ratios in Right-angled Triangles

One should not, at this point in the course of instruction, neglect to solve enough very simple, very basic exercises on the trigonometric ratios in right triangles. If one races by too quickly and notices down the road that students are uncertain so that the practice must be incorporated later, then the entire topic will have lost by that time its novelty and charm.

1. First level exercises
Draw the right triangle with side $\alpha = 7.2$ cm and angle $\beta = 53°$. Calculate the lengths of its other two sides (Fig. 31).

$$\frac{b}{a} = \tan\beta \qquad \frac{b}{7.2\,\text{cm}} = \tan 53° \mid \cdot 7.2\,\text{cm}$$

$$b = \tan 53° \cdot 7.2\,\text{cm} \qquad b = 9.55\,\text{cm}$$

$$\frac{a}{c} = \cos\beta$$

$$\frac{7.2\,\text{cm}}{c} = \cos 53° \mid \cdot c$$

$$7.2\,\text{cm} = \cos 53° \cdot c \mid : \cos 53°$$

$$c = \frac{7.2\,\text{cm}}{\cos 53°} = 11.96\,\text{cm}$$

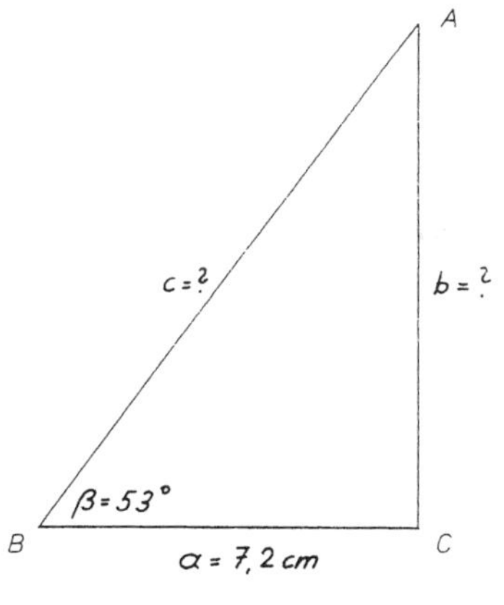

Fig. 31

If the triangle has been drawn as carefully as possible, the drawing and the calculation can be used to check one another; large errors can be detected at once. The slight variation between measurements and computed values continually underscore the fact that a diagram can never be absolutely perfect. One develops a fine sense, however, for what kinds of small errors tend to belong to imperfections in the diagram, and what kinds are to be regarded as red flags. When the diagrams and calculations are in sufficient agreement, then the student experiences confirmation in his work and is rewarded with a sense of certainty.

We conclude with a final computational check: does the Pythagorean theorem hold?

$$\sqrt{7.2^2 + 9.55^2} \stackrel{?}{=} 11.96$$

It holds to an accuracy of two decimal places.

With trigonometry, the study of triangles has been raised to a new level. We can now exactly determine the angles of Pythagorean triangles that are very familiar to us – for example, a triangle with sides $a = 9\,\text{cm}$, $b = 12\,\text{cm}$ and $c = 15\,\text{cm}$ (Fig. 32). What certainty and precision lies in calculation!

Measured values: $\beta \approx 53° \quad \alpha \approx 37°$

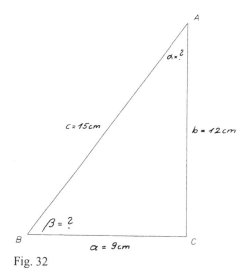

$$\tan\beta = \frac{b}{a} = \frac{12}{9} = \frac{4}{3} = 1.\overline{3}\ldots$$
$$\beta = \arctan 1.\overline{3}\ldots = 53.13°$$
$$\sin\beta = \frac{b}{c} = \frac{12}{15} = \frac{4}{5} = 0.8$$
$$\beta = \arcsin 0.8 = 53.13°$$
$$\cos\beta = \frac{a}{c} = \frac{9}{15} = \frac{3}{5} = 0.6$$
$$\beta = \arccos 0,6 = 53.13°$$

Fig. 32

2. Second level exercises

Thus far we have always drawn the legs of the right triangles horizontally and vertically; in this orientation we experience the right angle prominently. Naturally we can also lay the hypotenuse horizontally and use the Thales circle to determine the third vertex of the right triangle. When the height of this triangle is sketched in, a total of three similar right triangles are formed. In the resulting figure, there are many ways in which one can give two quantities and have the remainder deduced and calculated from them, for example, $c = 10\,\text{cm}$, $a = 40°$ (Fig. 33).

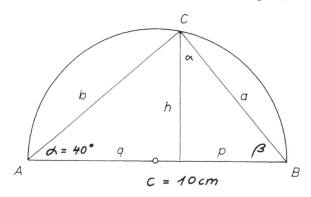

Fig. 33

1. $\beta = 50°$
2. $a = c \cdot \sin\alpha = 10 \cdot \sin 40° = 6.43\,\text{cm}$
3. $b = c \cdot \cos\alpha = 10 \cdot \cos 40° = 7.66\,\text{cm}$
4. $h = b \cdot \sin\alpha = 7.66 \cdot \sin 40° = 4.92\,\text{cm}$
5. $q = b \cdot \cos\alpha = 7.66 \cdot \cos 40° = 5.87\,\text{cm}$
6. $p = a \cdot \sin\alpha = 6.43 \cdot \sin 40° = 4.13\,\text{cm}$

Through various checks, the relationships between these values can be seen.

1. $p + q = 4.13 + 5.87 = 10$
2. $a \cdot b = 6.43 \cdot 7.66 = 49.25$ $(2F)$
   $c \cdot h = 10 \cdot 4.92 = 49.20$ $(2F)$
3. $p \cdot q = 4.13 \cdot 5.87 = 24.24$
   $h^2 = 4.92 = 24.21$

To these checks, one could also add the Pythagorean theorem and its corollaries.

So that the students can gain a sense for the opposing placement of angles and sides, and can learn to quickly and accurately recognize the sides in their roles as opposite, adjacent, and hypotenuse, the following exercise in Fig. 34 can always be used:

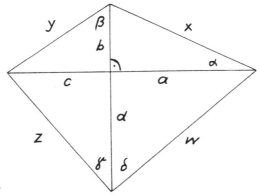

Fig. 34

What are the names of following ratios?

$$\frac{a}{b}, \quad \frac{b}{x}, \quad \frac{b}{x}, \quad \frac{c}{d}, \quad \dots$$

$(\cot\alpha, \sin\alpha, \cos\beta, \tan\gamma, \dots)$

Find the indicated the ratios:

$$\cos\alpha, \quad \tan\beta, \quad \sin\gamma, \quad \cot\delta, \quad \dots$$

$\left(\frac{a}{x}, \frac{c}{b}, \frac{c}{z}, \frac{d}{a}, \dots\right)$

Even at this level of computation it is worthwhile solving plenty of examples; all that follows will then be built upon a solid foundation. In order to be able to pose enough problems, I will provide a table with solved examples. The numbers that are underlined are the quantities to be given as assumed, although one could just as easily pick two of the other numbers. We will no longer demand a scaled diagram for each example, rather just a decent sketch that is sufficient for displaying and checking each calculated value.

α	β	a	b	c	h	p	q
°	°	cm	cm	cm	cm	cm	cm
23.0	67.0	6.5	15.4	16.7	6.0	2.6	14.1
17.2	72.8	4.7	15.2	15.9	4.5	1.4	14.5
45.6	44.4	7.1	7.0	10.0	5.0	5.1	4.9
55.8	34.2	7.6	5.2	9.2	4.3	6.3	2.9
36.9	53.1	5.0	6.7	8.3	4.0	3.0	5.3
20.7	69.3	6.5	17.3	18.5	6.1	2.3	16.2
56.0	34.0	13.3	8.9	16.0	7.4	11.0	5.0
64.3	25.7	12.9	6.2	14.4	5.6	11.7	2.7
23.6	66.4	5.0	11.5	12.5	4.6	2.0	10.5
28.5	61.5	6.7	12.3	14.0	5.9	3.2	10.8
40.9	49.1	4.6	5.3	7.0	3.5	3.0	4.0
39.4	50.6	5.5	6.7	8.7	4.3	3.5	5.2
58.4	31.6	12.4	7.6	14.6	6.5	10.6	4.0
67.4	22.6	2.7	1.1	2.9	1.0	2.5	0.4

3. Third level exercises

Because there are many applied exercises in the problem collections, I will only work through a single example here: in an isosceles triangle with sides $c = 8\,\text{cm}$, $a = b = 9\,\text{cm}$, calculate the radius of the inscribed circle, and that of the circumscribed circle (Fig. 35 and 36).

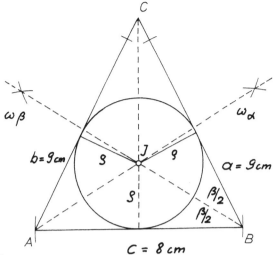

Fig. 35

1. Solution: (trigonometric)

$$\cos\beta = \frac{\frac{c}{2}}{a} = \frac{4}{9} = 0.\overline{4}\dots$$

$$\beta = \arccos 0.\overline{4}\dots = 63.61° \qquad \frac{\beta}{2} = 31.81°$$

$$\rho = \frac{c}{2}\cdot\tan\frac{\beta}{2} = 4\cdot\tan 31.81° = 2.48\,\text{cm}$$

2. Solution: (area)

We can compute the area of the triangle (Fig. 35) in two different ways: either with the help of the sides and the radius ρ, of the inscribed circle, or with c and h_c. The height h_c can be found from a and $\frac{c}{2}$ using the Pythagorean theorem. Comparing the two computations again yields the value $\rho = 2,48\,\text{cm}$. This strengthens the students' faith in the power and precision of the mathematical method.

$$A = \frac{c}{2}\cdot h = \frac{c}{2}\cdot\sqrt{a^2 - \left(\frac{c}{2}\right)^2} = 4\cdot\sqrt{65} = 4\cdot 8.06 = 32.24$$

$$A = \frac{a\cdot\rho}{2} + \frac{b\cdot\rho}{2} + \frac{c\cdot\rho}{2} = \rho\cdot\frac{a+b+c}{2} = \rho\cdot 13$$

$$\rho = \frac{32.42}{13} = 2.48\,\text{cm}$$

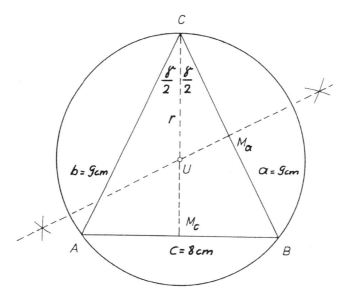

Fig. 36

Compute the radius r of the circumscribed circle

1. Solution: (trigonometric)

$$\sin\frac{\gamma}{2} = \frac{\frac{c}{2}}{a} = \frac{4}{9} = 0,\overline{4}$$

$$\frac{\gamma}{2} = \arcsin 0.\overline{4} = 26.39°$$

$$\cos\frac{\gamma}{2} = \frac{\frac{a}{2}}{r}$$

$$r = \frac{\frac{a}{2}}{\cos\frac{\gamma}{2}} = \frac{4.5}{\cos 26.39°} = 5.02\,\text{cm}$$

2. Solution: (similarity)

$$\triangle CUM_a \sim \triangle CBM_c: \quad \frac{r}{\frac{a}{2}} = \frac{a}{h} \Rightarrow r = \frac{a^2}{2h}$$

$$h = \sqrt{a^2 - \left(\frac{c}{2}\right)^2} = \sqrt{65} = 8.06$$

$$r = \frac{81}{2 \cdot 8.06} = 5.02\,\text{cm}$$

VI. The Law of Sines

Thus far, we have performed trigonometric calculations only on right triangles. One can easily ask such questions for general triangles: draw the triangle with side $c = 7.2$ cm and the angles $\alpha = 67°$ and $\beta = 61°$; compute the sides a and b (Fig. 37).

If the students begin with a false start as follows:

$$\sin\alpha = \frac{a}{c} \Rightarrow a = c \cdot \sin\alpha \Rightarrow a = 7.2 \cdot \sin 67° = 6.63\,\text{cm}$$

then they will immediately notice that something is wrong when they measure side a ($a \approx 8.4$ cm). Where is the error? Naturally, the given relationships between sides and angles are only valid in right triangles! But this triangle is not right! What should we do? We draw an altitude, so that right triangles are formed. The first attempt might be to draw the altitude to side c, but that would be a mistake; in the right triangles that are formed, none of the sides are known. Therefore we try it with a different altitude, for example the altitude to b. In triangle ABH_b we can compute the height h_b and with its help we can find the side a in triangle CBH_b; the angle γ is also known.

$$\sin\alpha = \frac{h_b}{c} \ \Big|\ \cdot c$$

$$h_b = c \cdot \sin\alpha = 7.2 \cdot \sin 67° = 6.63\,\text{cm}$$

$$\sin\gamma = \frac{h_b}{a}$$

$$a = \frac{h_b}{\sin\gamma} = \frac{6.63}{\sin 52°} = 8.41\,\text{cm}$$

This result obviously represents a confirmation and sharpening of the measured value $a \approx 8.4$ cm. Those who began with a false start were actually not calculating a, but rather h_b. Correspondingly, side b can be determined with the help of the altitude h_a. For this solution method, the students need not learn any new concepts; those they have learned for the right triangle are sufficient.

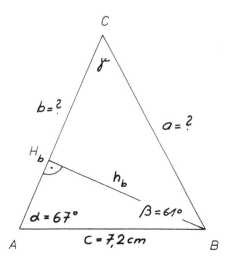

Fig. 37

We let the students solve a number of such exercises (one side and two angles given); naturally with different sides given. The thought begins to form, half-consciously, that actually we are always performing the same calculation. So we make this conjecture explicit: consider having no numbers given, just angles α, β, γ and side c, and having to compute a and b.

$$\sin\alpha = \frac{h_b}{c} \Rightarrow h_b = c \cdot \sin\alpha$$

$$\sin\gamma = \frac{h_b}{a} \Rightarrow a = \frac{h_b}{\sin\gamma} = \frac{c \cdot \sin\alpha}{\sin\gamma}$$

Similarly we find:

$$b = \frac{c \cdot \sin\beta}{\sin\gamma}.$$

The formula applied to Fig. 37

$$b = \frac{7.2 \cdot \sin 61°}{\sin 52°} = 7.99 \, \text{cm}$$

Measuring the drawing confirms this value. But these formulas are not easily remembered in their present form. Let's put them into an elegant form that can more easily be retained! If we divide the equations through, say, by c, we get

$$\frac{a}{c} = \frac{\sin\alpha}{\sin\gamma}$$

$$\frac{b}{c} = \frac{\sin\beta}{\sin\gamma}.$$

We recognize a common structure in these two proportions: *in an acute triangle, the ratio of any two sides equals the ratio of the sines of the opposite angles* (Law of Sines, Form I). To see that the equation

$$\frac{a}{b} = \frac{\sin\alpha}{\sin\beta}$$

holds, compute the case where side a or side b is given, along with the angles. If we are purely interested this relationship, and not in trying to solve a particular exercise, then it can also be proved with the aid of the altitude h_c in Fig. 37a.

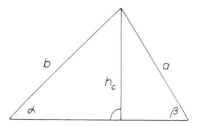

Fig. 37a

$$\sin \alpha = \frac{h_c}{b} \qquad \sin \beta = \frac{h_c}{a} \qquad \Rightarrow \qquad \frac{\sin \alpha}{\sin \beta} = \frac{\frac{h_c}{b}}{\frac{h_c}{a}} = \frac{a}{b}$$

The equations can be brought into the form:

$$\frac{a}{\sin \alpha} = \frac{c}{\sin \gamma} \qquad \frac{b}{\sin \beta} = \frac{c}{\sin \gamma}.$$

In short:

$$\frac{a}{\sin \alpha} = \frac{b}{\sin \beta} = \frac{c}{\sin \gamma}.$$

How do we express this relationship in words? These are *not* proportions, they are *quotients*. There are no lengths being set in relation to each other, and no sine values. The side lengths are being *divided* by the sine values of the opposite angles. The result of this division is a *length*; and it is always the *same*!

Law of Sines (Form II). *When the length of a side of an acute triangle is divided by the sine of the opposite angle, the resulting length is the same for all three sides.*

What is the resulting length? One would suspect that it bears some natural relationship to the given triangle. We pursue this question next.

Circumscribe a circle about a triangle with $c = 8\,\text{cm}$, $\alpha = 60°$, $\beta = 70°$, and calculate its radius (Fig. 38).
We solve this exercise with the aid of the central angle theorem: the central angle subtending side c (chord AB) is twice as large as the corresponding peripheral angle γ. (If the central angle theorem has not yet been covered in class, or has been forgotten, this would be an appropriate time to incorporate it or review it.)

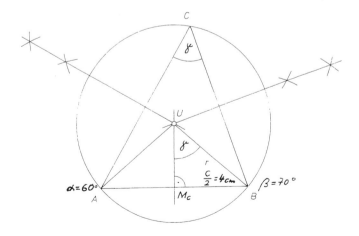

Fig. 38

From the triangle BM_cU it follows that:

$$\sin\gamma = \frac{\frac{c}{2}}{r} \Rightarrow r = \frac{\frac{c}{2}}{\sin\gamma}$$
$$= \frac{4}{\sin 50°}$$
$$= 5.22\,\text{cm}$$

and

$$r = \frac{c}{2} : \sin\gamma \quad\Rightarrow\quad d = c : \sin\gamma$$

Generally:

The quotient of a side divided by the sine of the opposite angle represents the diameter of the circle circumscribed about the triangle.

$$2r = \frac{a}{\sin\alpha} = \frac{b}{\sin\beta} = \frac{c}{\sin\gamma}$$

In Figure 39, we illustrate how this holds for all three sides.

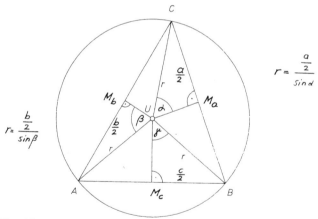

Fig. 39

Naturally we can also formulate it as follows:

$$\sin\alpha = \frac{a}{2r} \qquad \sin\beta = \frac{b}{2r} \qquad \sin\gamma = \frac{c}{2r}$$

Figure 40 depicts the last of these three formulas.

70

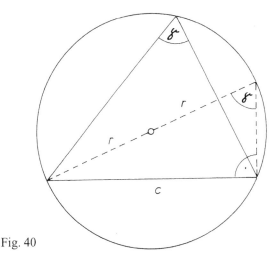

Fig. 40

If we had, as in Figure 37, used the first form of the Law of Sines to calculate the unknown sides, then we could use the second form to check our work. In Figure 37 it was given that: $c = 7.2$ cm, $\alpha = 67°$, $\beta = 61°$. From the first form of the Law of Sines, we calculated that $a = 8.41$ cm, $b = 7.99$ cm.

Check:

$$\frac{a}{\sin\alpha} = \frac{8.41\,\text{cm}}{\sin 67°} = 9.14\,\text{cm}$$

$$\frac{b}{\sin\beta} = \frac{7.99\,\text{cm}}{\sin 61°} = 9.14\,\text{cm}$$

$$\frac{c}{\sin\gamma} = \frac{7.20\,\text{cm}}{\sin 52°} = 9.14\,\text{cm}.$$

Up until now, we have only considered acute triangles. Does the Law of Sines hold for obtuse triangles as well? Suppose the angle α is obtuse (Fig. 41).

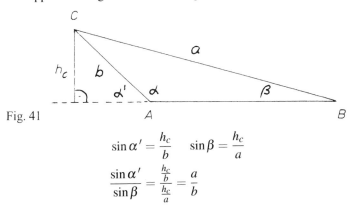

Fig. 41

$$\sin\alpha' = \frac{h_c}{b} \qquad \sin\beta = \frac{h_c}{a}$$

$$\frac{\sin\alpha'}{\sin\beta} = \frac{\frac{h_c}{b}}{\frac{h_c}{a}} = \frac{a}{b}$$

In place of the sine of the obtuse angle α, there appears the sine of the supplementary angle α'. What would be the sine of the obtuse angle? At this point, we consider the relationships not only in the right triangle, but in the circle (Fig. 42).

71

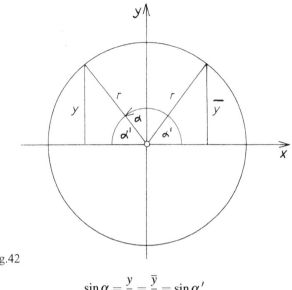

Fig.42

$$\sin \alpha = \frac{y}{r} = \frac{\bar{y}}{r} = \sin \alpha'$$

Figure 42 shows the convenience of setting the sine of obtuse angles equal to the sine of the supplementary angle, so that the Law of Sines will continue to hold as stated:

$$\frac{\sin \alpha}{\sin \beta} = \frac{a}{b}.$$

And equivalently (Fig. 43):

$$\sin \gamma' = \frac{\frac{c}{2}}{r} = \sin \gamma \quad \text{(Fig. 43)}$$

$$\frac{c}{\sin \gamma} = 2r$$

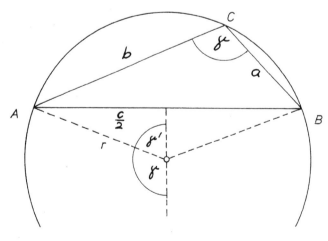

Fig. 43

Two fundamental problems can be solved using the Law of Sines:

1. Problem: One side of a triangle and all three angles are given (this problem was our starting point).

2. Problem: Two sides of a triangle and the angle opposite the larger is given.

1. Example: $a = 6.1\,\text{cm}$, $b = 4.8\,\text{cm}$, $\alpha = 58°$ (Fig. 44)

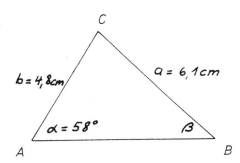

Fig. 44

$$\frac{\sin\beta}{\sin\alpha} = \frac{b}{a} = \frac{4.8}{6.1}$$

$$\sin\beta = \frac{4.8}{6.1} \cdot \sin 58° = 0.667...$$

$$b = \arcsin 0.667... = 41.86°$$

or:

$$2r = \frac{a}{\sin\alpha} = \frac{6.1\,\text{cm}}{\sin 58°} = 7.19...\text{cm}$$

$$\sin\beta = \frac{b}{2r} = \frac{4.8}{7.19} = 0.667...$$

$$\beta = \arcsin 0.667... = 41.86°$$

$$\gamma = 80.14°$$

$$c = 2r \cdot \sin\gamma = 7.19\,\text{cm} \cdot \sin 80.14° = 7.09\,\text{cm}$$

2. Example: $a = 5.6\,\text{cm}$, $b = 9.3\,\text{cm}$, $\beta = 125°$ (Fig. 45)

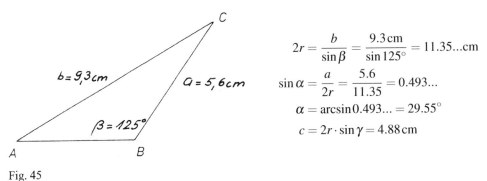

$$2r = \frac{b}{\sin\beta} = \frac{9.3\,\text{cm}}{\sin 125°} = 11.35...\text{cm}$$

$$\sin\alpha = \frac{a}{2r} = \frac{5.6}{11.35} = 0.493...$$

$$\alpha = \arcsin 0.493... = 29.55°$$

$$c = 2r \cdot \sin\gamma = 4.88\,\text{cm}$$

Fig. 45

73

It is very instructive to give two sides of a triangle and the angle opposite the shorter of these two sides. Two triangles are determined by these assumptions. It is possible to construct and calculate both of them.

Example: $a = 4.5\,\text{cm}$, $b = 7\,\text{cm}$, $\alpha = 35°$ (Fig. 46)

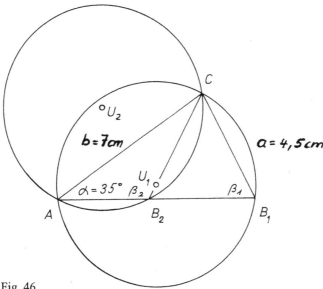

Fig. 46

$$2r = \frac{a}{\sin\alpha} = \frac{4.5\,\text{cm}}{\sin 35°} = 7.845...\text{cm}$$

$$\sin\beta = \frac{b}{2r} = \frac{7}{7.845...} = 0.892...$$

$$\beta = \arcsin 0.892... \Rightarrow \beta_1 = 63.15° \quad \beta_2 = 116.85°$$

$$\gamma_1 = 81.85° \quad \gamma_2 = 28.15°$$

$$c_1 = 2r \cdot \sin\gamma_1 = 7.77\,\text{cm}$$

$$c_2 = 2r \cdot \sin\gamma_2 = 3.70\,\text{cm}$$

It is quite satisfying that two solutions appear, not only in the computations but also in the construction. Corresponding to a positive value of sine, there are two supplementary angles, one in the first quadrant and the other in the second. It is also noteworthy that the radius of the circumscribed circle for both triangles is the same, namely 3.92 cm. As a check, one can construct both of these circles.

The second form of the Law of Sines can be illustrated on the circumscribed circle in a very satisfactory manner. Can we find a drawing on which the first form can be just as easily illustrated (Fig. 47)? We mark off the length of side a along side b and deduce the ratios from similar triangles that share vertex C.

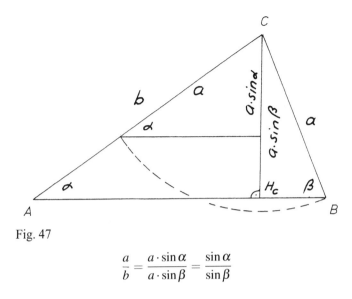

Fig. 47

$$\frac{a}{b} = \frac{a \cdot \sin \alpha}{a \cdot \sin \beta} = \frac{\sin \alpha}{\sin \beta}$$

VII. The Law of Cosines

Rudolf Steiner placed great value on a thorough treatment of this theorem. In his pedagogical lectures he often refers to it as the Theorem of Carnot. It was important to him that students recognize the Pythagorean Theorem, with which they have long been familiar, as a special case of the Law of Cosines which is a general context that encompasses far more.

Once again we can proceed in such a way that the students discover the results for themselves in the context of a basic problem. Exercise: In a triangle with sides $a = 8\,\text{cm}$, $b = 7\,\text{cm}$, and angle $\gamma = 70°$, compute the length of side c.

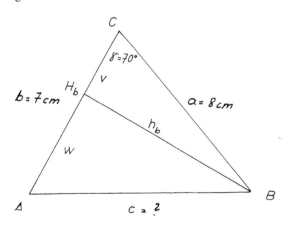

Fig. 48

The students will first try to solve the problem with the help of the Law of Sines. But no matter how they may try to apply it, it will not lead them to their goal; they will always be confronted with a pair of unknowns. We must find a new approach that is fundamentally different: We must resort back to right triangles by constructing a height, such as h_b. In triangle BCH_b we can calculate h_b and v. Then by applying the Pythagorean Theorem to triangle BH_bA we can find the length of side c.

$$h_b = a \cdot \sin \gamma$$
$$= 8\,\text{cm} \cdot 70° = 7.52\,\text{cm}$$
$$v = a \cdot \cos \gamma$$
$$= 8\,\text{cm} \cdot \cos 70° = 2.74\,\text{cm}$$
$$w = b - v$$
$$= 7\,\text{cm} - 2.74\,\text{cm} = 4.26\,\text{cm}$$
$$c^2 = w^2 + h_b^2$$
$$= 4.26^2\,\text{cm}^2 + 7.52^2\,\text{cm}^2 = 74.698\,\text{cm}^2$$
$$c = \sqrt{74.698\,\text{cm}^2} = 8.64\,\text{cm}$$

Measurement of the corresponding segment in the construction shows that this calculated value is reasonable.

At first we let the calculations be computed through numerically, and leave aside the task of finding a general algebraic formulation. In this way, the students can find their way to the results with relatively little assistance. Then we let the students solve several more such basic problems (where they are given two sides and the angle between them). They master the numerical calculations after just a few examples, even when different pairs of sides and the corresponding angles are given. At the end, we pose the question generally:

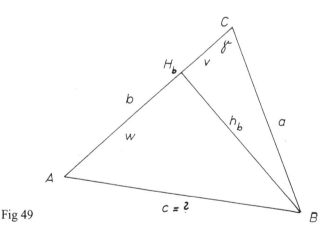

Fig 49

Try to compute the length of side c from sides a and b, and angle γ, without being given specific numerical values. The slower students continue to compute with specific examples while the quicker students will turn to the general problem. We circulate around the classroom as they work, observing the students as they make tentative attempts, hit upon the right way, or get stuck somewhere – a helpful tip and they can find their own way further. When they reach their goal –

the general statement – they always feel internal satisfaction. The calculation can be organized as follows (Fig. 49).

$$h_b = a \cdot \sin\gamma \quad v = a \cdot \cos\gamma$$
$$w = b - v = b - a \cdot \cos\gamma$$
$$c^2 = w^2 + h_b^2 = (b - a \cdot \cos\gamma)^2 + (a \cdot \sin\gamma)^2$$
$$= b^2 - 2ab\cos\gamma + a^2\cos^2\gamma + a^2\sin^2\gamma$$
$$= b^2 - 2ab\cos\gamma + a^2\left(\cos^2\gamma + \sin^2\gamma\right) \text{ with } \left(\cos^2\gamma + \sin^2\gamma\right) = 1$$
$$= a^2 + b^2 - 2ab\cos\gamma$$

In case the students do not know the trigonometric form of the Pythagorean Theorem, it can be incorporated at this point. The fact that

$$a^2\cos^2\gamma + a^2\sin^2\gamma = a^2$$

can be seen on the triangle BH_bC, since $v^2 + h_b^2 = a^2$. The calculation can also be shortened to:

$$c^2 = w^2 + h_b^2 = (b - v)^2 + h_b^2$$
$$= b^2 - 2bv + v^2 + h_b^2$$
$$= b^2 - 2bv + a^2 \quad \text{with } v^2 + h_b^2 = a^2$$
$$c^2 = a^2 + b^2 - 2bv$$
$$= a^2 + b^2 - 2ab\cos\gamma$$

If numbers are given for a, b, and γ, we can plug them into this expression directly, saving us the steps in the computation that led to c^2. But this is only a simplistic use of the formula; we haven't yet appreciated its depth. It is now our job to familiarize the students with it on a deeper level.

As in the Pythagorean Theorem, this formula relates the squares of the sides of the triangle! But notice it is an acute triangle this time! We draw an acute triangle with the squares on its sides (Fig. 50, right).

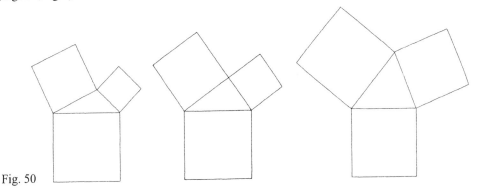

Fig. 50

To gain a better overview, we also draw the diagram for an obtuse triangle and, in between, for a right triangle; all with the same base c. The middle figure is familiar. The squares on the legs are organically related with one another; each of the legs can be extended, unbroken, into a side of the other square. If we have only ever drawn the side squares on right triangles before, then the other two figures appear deformed to us. The figure on the left is squeezed together; the upper squares are diminished. The figure on the right has extended upward beyond a right angle; the upper squares are oversized. The diminishment and oversizing can be more plainly seen on isosceles triangles (Figure 51).

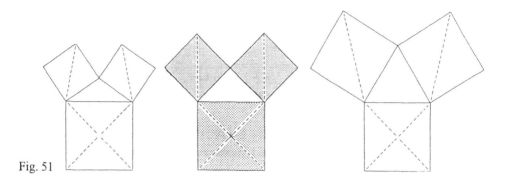

Fig. 51

We know that in a right triangle, the squares on the legs sum exactly to the area of the square on the hypotenuse: $c^2 = a^2 + b^2$. In an obtuse triangle, $c^2 > a^2 + b^2$, while in an acute triangle, $c^2 < a^2 + b^2$. If equality is to hold in the latter relation, then a correction term must be subtracted from the area $a^2 + b^2$. From the calculations, we know that this correction term is $2ab\cos\gamma$, or equivalently, $2bv$. Can we visualize this on the figure of the acute triangle? We recall the corollary of the Pythagorean Theorem (Fig. 52).

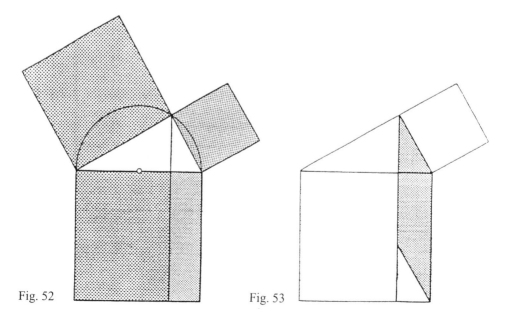

Fig. 52   Fig. 53

We can see that the square on the right leg has the same area as the rightmost rectangle inside the square on the hypotenuse, by shearing, rotating, and shearing: from Fig. 52 to Fig. 53 we shear in the direction of the altitude; from Fig. 53 to Fig. 54 we rotate $90°$ around point B; from Fig. 54 to Fig. 55 we shear in the direction of side b.

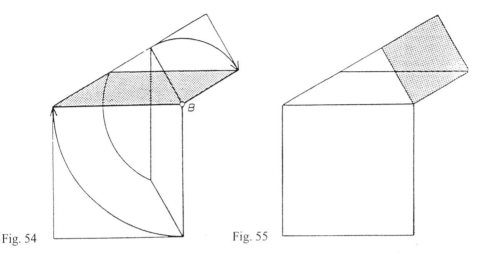

Fig. 54   Fig. 55

The same argument applies to the left square and the rectangle on the left.

What would this proof look like if we applied it to an acute triangle? We extend the height h_c through the lower square and transform the leftmost rectangle (Figures 56 through 59).

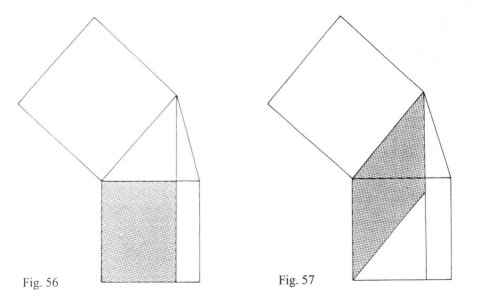

Fig. 56   Fig. 57

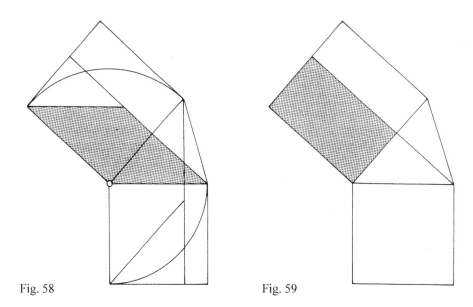

Fig. 58   Fig. 59

The resulting area is not that of the left square, but rather just a portion of it, namely, the rectangle that is bounded by the height h_b. If we follow this process through on the right side, rather than the left, we reach the same conclusion: the rectangles on the lower right and on the right side with the common vertex B, bounded by the heights h_c and h_a must have the same area. Similarly for the two rectangles above with the common vertex C. In Figures 60 and 61, the two congruent parallelograms are depicted before and after being rotated about point C.

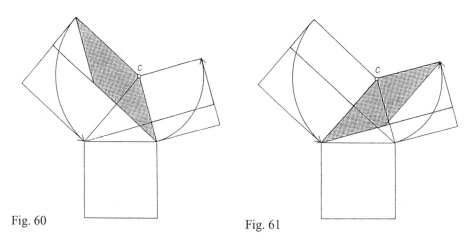

Fig. 60   Fig. 61

The results in summary: *When the three squares on the sides of an acute triangle are drawn, and the altitudes are extended through them, there are six rectangles formed; any two that meet at a corner are equal in size* (Fig. 62).

I have been unable to find a name for this result in the literature; in class I have typically referred to it as the Rectangle Theorem. It is the purely geometric content of the Law of Cosines; the law itself is the quantitative formulation of the Rectangle Theorem.

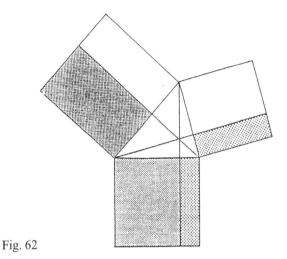

Fig. 62

The equality of areas of a pair of rectangles, such as the two upper ones, can also be seen by way of similarity (Fig. 63).

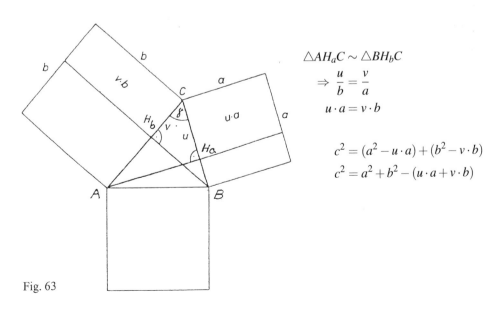

$$\triangle AH_aC \sim \triangle BH_bC$$

$$\Rightarrow \frac{u}{b} = \frac{v}{a}$$

$$u \cdot a = v \cdot b$$

$$c^2 = (a^2 - u \cdot a) + (b^2 - v \cdot b)$$
$$c^2 = a^2 + b^2 - (u \cdot a + v \cdot b)$$

Fig. 63

And lastly, the segments u and v can be calculated.

$$\cos\gamma = \frac{u}{b} \Rightarrow u = b \cdot \cos\gamma$$

$$a \cdot u = a \cdot b \cdot \cos\gamma$$

$$\cos\gamma = \frac{v}{a} \Rightarrow v = a \cdot \cos\gamma$$

$$b \cdot v = b \cdot a \cdot \cos\gamma$$

$$\Rightarrow c^2 = a^2 + b^2 - 2ab\cos\gamma$$

This equation has now been thoroughly examined. But naturally, the Law of Cosines can be formulated for each of the three sides (Fig. 64).

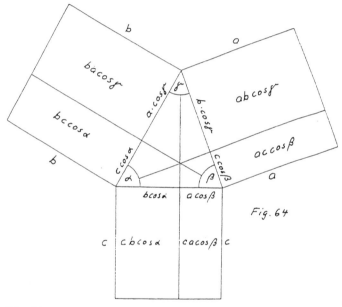

Fig. 64

$$a^2 = b^2 + c^2 - 2bc\cos\alpha$$

$$b^2 = c^2 + a^2 - 2ca\cos\beta$$

$$c^2 = a^2 + b^2 - 2ab\cos\gamma$$

In case one didn't point it out already in the Law of Sines, now is a good occasion to mention the principle of cyclic substitution. If we slide point C in Figure 62 along the altitude h_c downward until it meets the Thales circle with diameter c, then the two upper rectangles (white) become ever narrower; they disappear the moment the triangle becomes right and the altitudes h_a and h_b

become the legs b and a (as in Fig. 52). From the Rectangle Theorem we obtain the corollary to the Pythagorean Theorem. What happens if the point C continues further and the triangle becomes obtuse? The altitudes h_a and h_b then exit the triangle, entering side squares as they pass through a and b (Figures 65 and 66).

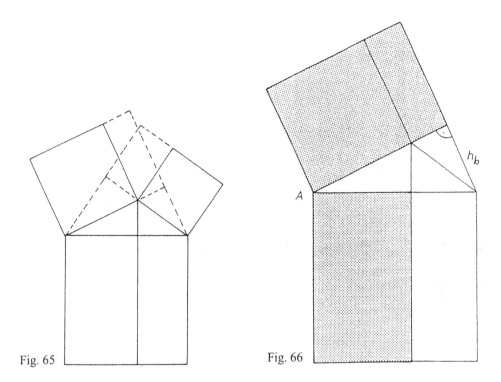

Fig. 65   Fig. 66

The side rectangles that share areas with the lower rectangles protrude beyond the upper side squares, partially overlapping, and the two upper rectangles with common point C extend as excess regions next to the squares on sides a and b.

We can see in Figure 67 that the two excess regions have the same size. From similar triangles, we have:

$$\frac{u}{b} = \frac{v}{a} \Rightarrow u \cdot a = v \cdot b$$

The fact that the other two pairs of rectangles have equal areas can similarly be deduced by similar triangles, for example, in Figure 66. The lower rectangle in Figure 66 can also be sheared along h_c, rotated about A, and sheared along h_b to become the upper rectangle. It follows that the Rectangle Theorem also holds for obtuse triangles; the rectangles that meet at point C just happen to lie inside the side rectangles on the left and right.

83

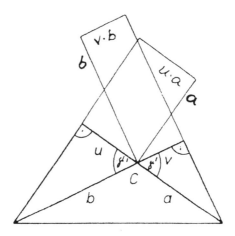

Fig 67

So what form does the corresponding calculation take in the case of the obtuse triangle? From Figure 67 we obtain:

$$u = b \cdot \cos \gamma' \quad \text{and} \quad v = a \cdot \cos \gamma'.$$

Thus the upper rectangles have area:

$$a \cdot b \cdot \cos \gamma' \quad \text{or} \quad b \cdot a \cdot \cos \gamma'.$$

The square under the base is as large as the sum of the two side rectangles; and these are as large as the squares on sides a and b enlarged around the upper rectangle. Thus it holds that:

$$c^2 = a^2 + a \cdot b \cdot \cos \gamma' + b^2 + b \cdot a \cdot \cos \gamma'$$
$$= a^2 + b^2 + 2ab \cos \gamma'$$

The excess of c^2 over $a^2 + b^2$ is in the amount $2ab \cos \gamma'$. Again we see that in the obtuse triangle, the supplementary angle appears γ' in place of the obtuse angle γ.

What would then be the cosine of the obtuse angle? Again we turn to the ratios in the unit circle (Fig. 68).

In the first quadrant we have

$$\cos \gamma' = \frac{x'}{r}.$$

In the second quadrant,

$$\cos \gamma = \frac{x}{r}.$$

Because $x = -x'$ it follows that:

$$\cos \gamma = -\cos \gamma'.$$

84

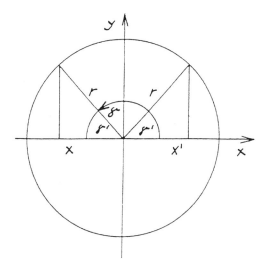

Fig. 68

If we let the acute angle γ' grow beyond $90°$ and outside the first quadrant to γ, then the x-coordinate changes from positive x' through zero to the negative x. Because $\cos\gamma = -\cos\gamma'$, it holds that:

$$c^2 = a^2 + b^2 + 2ab\cos\gamma'$$
$$= a^2 + b^2 - 2ab\cos\gamma.$$

The Law of Cosines can therefore be formulated for obtuse triangles just as it was for acute triangles. And even in the case of the right triangle it holds in the same form; setting $\cos 90° = 0$ reduces the Law of Cosines to the familiar Pythagorean Theorem.

Much is gained if we can bring students to experience that *the Pythagorean Theorem is simply an intermediate stage of an entire process.*

When the point C in Figure 69 descends to the Thales circle and passes below it, then not only do c and c^2 change, but all the angles and the sides a and b and their squares; *but in each position of the point C, the identity holds that*:

$$c^2 = a^2 + b^2 - 2ab\cos\gamma.$$

And this is true even though there are many changing quantities! We can continually be amazed by the persistent validity of this relationship. The students experience that the Pythagorean Theorem itself is merely an isolated observation; it can be generalized to a much broader truth. They begin to ponder the weighty question: is the same true of other perceptions? Are all our observations capable of generalization? They have many experiences with such generalizations: when, in projective geometry, the concept of a quadrangle is broadened to that of an abstract quadrangle, and the polar concept of an abstract quadrilateral is introduced; when it is recognized that trapezoids, parallelograms, rectangles, and squares are special forms of abstract quadrangles or quadrilaterals

85

in which certain elements are located infinitely far away. It would be particularly nice, if we could show them that axial and central reflection are special cases of harmonic reflection.

It is worth following how the base points H_a and H_b of the altitudes move in Figure 69 when point C slides down along altitude h_c: these base points move along the Thales circle; on the Thales circle itself, the four points C, H, H_a and H_b all coincide, separate again and exchange positions.

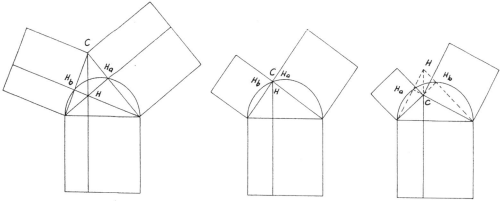

Fig. 69

To conclude, we let the students solve the fourth basic exercise: all three sides of a triangle are given, the angles are to be calculated. Example: $a = 9\,\text{cm}$, $b = 8\,\text{cm}$, $c = 7\,\text{cm}$ (Fig. 70).

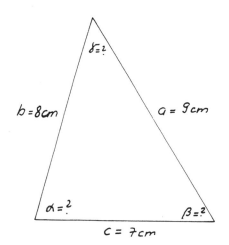

Fig. 70

We measure: $\alpha \approx 73°$, $\beta \approx 58°$, $\gamma \approx 48°$, whose sum is $\approx 179°$. The angles are calculated:

$$c^2 = a^2 + b^2 - 2ab\cos\gamma$$
$$49 = 81 + 64 - 144\cos\gamma \mid +144\cos\gamma - 49$$

$$144\cos\gamma = 96 \mid : 144$$

$$\cos\gamma = \frac{96}{144} = \frac{2}{3} = 0,\overline{6}$$

$$\gamma = \arccos 0.\overline{6} = 48.19°$$

$$a^2 = b^2 + c^2 - 2bc\cos\alpha$$

$$81 = 64 + 49 - 112\cos\alpha \mid +112\cos\alpha - 81$$

$$112\cos\alpha = 32 \mid : 112$$

$$\cos\alpha = \frac{32}{112} = \frac{2}{7}$$

$$\alpha = \arccos\frac{2}{7} = 73.40°$$

$$b^2 = c^2 + a^2 - 2ca\cos\beta$$

$$64 = 49 + 81 - 126\cos\beta \mid +126\cos\beta - 64$$

$$126\cos\beta = 66 \mid : 126$$

$$\cos\beta = \frac{66}{126} = \frac{11}{21}$$

$$\beta = \arccos\frac{11}{21} = 58.41°$$

And we find the sum to be:

$$\alpha + \beta + \gamma = 73.40° + 58.41° + 48.19°$$

$$= 180.00°$$

We compute all three angles with the Law of Cosines and use the angle sum to check our work. Naturally we must make it clear to the students that the angles are only determined to 2 decimal places; the fact that the sum is exactly $180°$ only means that the roundings cancel each other out.

Why not solve the general formula for $\cos\alpha$, $\cos\beta$, and $\cos\gamma$? Why do we first substitute in and then simplify? It has been my experience with nearly all my 10th graders that the students find such a formulation confusing at first in the general case. The numerical simplification is easier for them. After a few examples, they can then find the general case:

$$c^2 = a^2 + b^2 - 2ab\cos\gamma \mid +2ab\cos\gamma - c^2$$

$$2ab\cos\gamma = a^2 + b^2 - c^2 \quad \mid : 2ab$$

$$\cos\gamma = \frac{a^2 + b^2 - c^2}{2ab}$$

In the numbers we find conditions for acute, right, or obtuse angles:

$$\text{If } a^2 + b^2 - c^2 > 0$$
$$\Rightarrow \cos \gamma > 0 \quad \Rightarrow \gamma \text{ acute}$$
$$\text{if } a^2 + b^2 - c^2 = 0$$
$$\Rightarrow \cos \gamma = 0 \quad \Rightarrow \gamma \text{ right}$$
$$\text{if } a^2 + b^2 - c^2 < 0$$
$$\Rightarrow \cos \gamma < 0 \quad \Rightarrow \gamma \text{ obtuse.}$$

Similarly it holds that:

$$\cos \alpha = \frac{b^2 + c^2 - a^2}{2bc}$$
$$\cos \beta = \frac{c^2 + a^2 - b^2}{2ca}$$

2. Example: $c = 9\,\text{cm}$, $a = 5\,\text{cm}$, $b = 6\,\text{cm}$

$$\cos \gamma = \frac{a^2 + b^2 - c^2}{2ab}$$
$$= \frac{25 + 36 - 81}{2 \cdot 5 \cdot 6} = \frac{-20}{60} = \frac{-1}{3}$$
$$\Rightarrow \gamma = 109.47°$$

$$\cos \alpha = \frac{b^2 + c^2 - a^2}{2bc}$$
$$= \frac{36 + 81 - 25}{2 \cdot 6 \cdot 9} = \frac{92}{108} = \frac{23}{27}$$
$$\Rightarrow \alpha = 31.59°$$

$$\cos \beta = \frac{c^2 + a^2 - b^2}{2ca}$$
$$= \frac{81 + 25 - 36}{2 \cdot 9 \cdot 5} = \frac{70}{90} = \frac{7}{9}$$
$$\Rightarrow \beta = 38.94°$$
$$\alpha + \beta + \gamma = 180.00°$$

Two of the fundamental exercises are solved with the Law of Sines, the other two with the Law of Cosines. These exercises are related to the congruence theorems. Triangles are congruent when they agree in

- one side and 2 adjacent angles (Law of Sines),

- two sides and the angle opposite the larger (Law of Sines),
- two sides and the included angle (Law of Cosines),
- the three sides (Law of Cosines).

We conclude with a table with examples of the third and fourth fundamental exercises:

a	b	γ	c^2	c
cm	cm	°	cm^2	cm
10	5	35	43.00848	6.6
5	4	74	29.9745	5.47
7	9	63	72.7972	8.53
5	6	40	15.0373	3.88
6	4	120	76	8.72
5	7	135	123.4975	11.11
6,3	4.6	57	29.2827	5.41

a	b	c	$\cos\alpha$	α	$\cos\beta$	β	$\cos\gamma$	γ
cm	cm	cm		°		°		°
7	6	5	$\frac{1}{5}$	78.5	$\frac{19}{35}$	57.1	$\frac{5}{7}$	44.4
10	9	8	$\frac{5}{16}$	71.8	$\frac{83}{160}$	58.8	$\frac{13}{20}$	49.5
12	13	11	$\frac{73}{143}$	59.3	$\frac{4}{11}$	68.7	$\frac{24}{39}$	52
6	7	10	$\frac{113}{140}$	36.2	$\frac{29}{40}$	43.5	$\frac{-5}{28}$	100.3
11	5	8	$\frac{-2}{5}$	114	$\frac{10}{11}$	24.6	$\frac{41}{55}$	41.8
9	10	11	$\frac{7}{11}$	50.5	$\frac{17}{33}$	59	$\frac{1}{3}$	70.5

The Special Cases of the Law of Cosines

Markus Hünig

We consider the Law of Cosines in a triangle where the angle γ gradually increases from $0°$ to $180°$. We recall the following values of cosine:

$$\cos 0° = 1 \quad \cos 90° = 0 \quad \cos 180° = -1.$$

1. When $\gamma = 0°$, we have

$$\begin{aligned} c^2 &= a^2 + b^2 - 2ab \cdot 1 \\ &= a^2 - 2ab + b^2 \\ &= (a-b)^2; \end{aligned}$$

and we can see from the diagram that $c = a - b$.

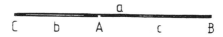

2. As γ opens, the point C rises; the sides a and b remain unchanged, and c increases.

3. Then γ opens further.

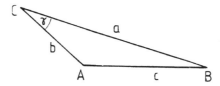

4. When $\gamma = 90°$ we have

$$\begin{aligned} c^2 &= a^2 + b^2 - 2ab \cdot \cdot 0 \\ &= a^2 + b^2 \text{ (Pythagorean theorem)}. \end{aligned}$$

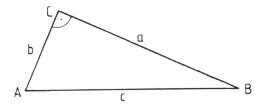

5. Then γ stretches further...

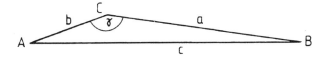

... and eventually becomes a straight angle.
Here we have

$$c^2 = a^2 + b^2 - 2ab \cdot (-1)$$
$$= a^2 + 2ab + b^2$$
$$= (a+b)^2;$$

and we can see from the diagram that $c = a + b$.

For $\gamma = 0°$ and $\gamma = 180°$ we obtain the binomial expansions for $(a-b)^2$ and $(a+b)^2$; but it is also clear that in the first case $c = a - b$, and in the latter case $c = a + b$. For $\gamma = 90°$ we obtain the well known Pythagorean theorem.

The Law of Cosines is therefore a very general, comprehensive result; the binomial expansions for $(a+b)^2$ and $(a-b)^2$ are both contained as special cases, as well as the Pythagorean theorem.

The Higher Calculations

Markus Hünig

Preliminary Remarks

The tenth grade should provide 16- and 17 year-old mathematics students with the experience that, beginning from clear and direct observations, and through strict application of the known rules, one can expand the basic calculation methods so far that, with them, an enormous variety of systems and processes in nature and society can be encompassed[1]. Trigonometry and the corresponding surveying project are well suited to this goal, as is the treatment of the higher calculations. Not only is this clear realization particularly important, but so are a conceptual and perceptual grasp of linear growth, on the one hand, and of exponential or logarithmic growth on the other. This contrast will therefore be given a somewhat broader emphasis right from the beginning.

The various examples cited throughout this work are limited to what is necessary for the students' lesson books and they require, of course, an assortment of supplementary practice problems; experience shows that it is convenient for students to keep these in an exercise book that is separate from the main lesson book (which is to serve as reference in the following years).

If the lesson book is to serve well in its role as a reference, then the text must be essentially free of errors and be complete in its logical and pedagogical development. Therefore, the author only lets his students freely compose the text under exceptional circumstances; much more commonly, the suggestions of the students from the classroom conversation are incorporated, with the help of the teacher, into as concise a text as possible. In fact, substantial portions of the present text can also be traced back to discussions from the classroom in the Waldorf school in Mülheim.

The present work encompasses a four-week lesson block; in case this much time is not available, some of the parts can be covered in the weekly math lessons that follow. For example, the last chapter is well suited for this. It is also possible that continued fractions and other approximation techniques have been introduced in the 9th grade[2], in which case they would require only a brief review here. Further recommendations for shortening the material are denoted with italics in the overview. The traditional work with logarithms has, since the introduction of the calculator, lost some of its practical significance; the point here has more to do with familiarizing the students with the topic and having them get a feel for it. If the class has access to a set of sliderules, then it is helpful to have them play around with them. To give the topic of logarithms a useful application, the solving of simple exponential equations is thoroughly appropriate.

I. Arithmetic and Geometric Sequences

1. Introduction

Mr. Maurer and Mr. Drechsler both have hourly wages of $23. Mr. Maurer agrees with his employer that his wage will increase by $1.50 each year; Mr. Drechsler agrees to a yearly increase

---

[1] In the 11th grade this process is carried even further: thought begins to exceed the limits of the imagination.

[2] see, for example, the article from P. Baum in the Topics book for the 9th grade, "The Euclidean algorithm and continued fractions"

of 5%

1. How do the hourly wages grow over the next 20 years?

2. How many years must pass until the two have earned the same amount, if, each year, they are paid for 2,200 hours of work (no interest earned)?

Solution:

1. The salary of Mr. Maurer is easy to calculate:

   1st year: $23

   2nd year: $23 + $1.50 = $24.50; etc.

   so the wage must be increased from year to year by the fixed amount of $1.50.

   With Mr. Drechsler we must consider the following:

   1st year: $23

   2nd year:

$$\$23 + 5\% \text{ of } \$23 = \$23 + \frac{5}{100} \cdot \$23$$
$$= \$23 + 0.05 \cdot \$23$$
$$= (1 + 0.05) \cdot \$23$$
$$= 1.05 \cdot \$23 = \$24.15$$

and correspondingly, for the third year:

$$1.05 \cdot \$24.15 = \$25.3575 \approx \$25.36$$

From year to year, then, the wage must be multiplied by a factor of 1.05. With that, we obtain the following wages:

year	Maurer	Drechsler
1	23	23
2	24.5	24.15
3	26	25.36
4	27.5	26.63
5	29	27.96
6	30.5	29.36
7	32	30.83
8	33.5	32.37
9	35	33.99
10	36.5	35.69
11	38	37.47
12	39.5	39.34
13	41	41.31
14	42.5	43.88
15	44	45.55
16	45.5	47.83

2. We see that at first, Mr. Maurer is clearly better off; but after 13 years, Mr. Drechsler has caught up in wage and earns more from that time forward.

3. Now we must calculate the yearly earnings for each year and then add up the incomes of the individual years:

year	Maurer	Drechsler
1	50,600	50,600
2	104,500	103,730
3	161,700	159,522
4	22,200	218,108
5	286,000	279,620
6	353,100	344,212
7	423,500	412,038
8	497,200	483,252
9	574,200	558,030
10	654,500	636,548
11	738,100	718,982
12	825,000	805,530
13	915,200	896,412
14	1,008,700	991,848
15	1,105,500	1,092,058
16	1,205,600	1,197,284
17	1,309,000	1,307,768
18	1,415,700	1,423,774
19	1,525,700	1,545,588
20	1,639,000	1,673,496
21	1,755,600	1,807,806
22	1,875,500	1,948,826
23	1,998,700	2,096,908
24	2,125,200	2,252,404

Now it becomes clear: After 18 years Mr. Drechsler has earned more in total than Mr. Maurer. Although it took 13 years for Mr. Drechsler to reach the same hourly wage as Mr. Maurer, it only takes 5 years after that until his net earnings have exceeded the other's!

We are dealing with two very different forms of growth here.
With Mr. Maurer, the wage grows each year by a constant amount. The wage in the $(n+1)$-st year can be calculated as

$$\text{Wage in the } n\text{-th year} + \text{increase amount.}$$

The resulting sums form what is called an arithmetic sequence. Generally in such sequences, the first term is labelled a_1, the second a_2, and so on; the general n-th term of the sequence is denoted by a_n.

In our example,
$$a_1 = 23; \; a_2 = 23 + 1.5 = 24.5; \; a_3 = 24.5 + 1.5 = 26$$

Two consecutive terms therefore differ by the same amount, that is, their difference is always the same (in this case, 1.5). Thus we call this amount the growth quantity d. Generally, it holds that:

$$a_2 = a_1 + d$$
$$a_3 = a_2 + d$$
$$a_3 = a_2 + d$$
$$a_{n+1} = a_n + d$$

The wage increase Mr. Drechsler agreed to, however, is such that the amount by which the salary increases is always dependent on the salary at that given moment. The higher his wage is, the larger the amount of his raise will be. The amount by which his wage grows is *not* constant.

More significant is the particular percentage by which his annual raise is increased; this has the effect of multiplying the wage by a particular factor (see the computation above). It holds, namely, that:

$$a_1 = 23$$
$$a_2 = 23 \cdot 1.05 = 24.15$$
$$a_3 = 24.15 \cdot 1.05 = 25.3575 \approx 25.36.$$

Here, the ratio of two successive terms is constant:

$$\frac{a_2}{a_1} = \frac{a_3}{a_2} = 1.05.$$

Such a sequence is called a geometric sequence. The constant ratio (the growth factor, here 1.05) we denote by q (to remind us of "quotient"). Generally it holds that:

$$a_2 = a_1 \cdot q$$
$$a_3 = a_2 \cdot q$$
$$a_4 = a_3 \cdot q$$
$$a_{n+1} = a_n \cdot q$$

The $(n+1)$-st term of a geometric sequence is calculated from the n-th term by multiplication by the growth factor q.

A few examples:

Arithmetic sequences:

1. $a_1 = 5$; $d = 0.8$; these give: $a_2 = 5.8$; $a_3 = 6.6$; $a_4 = 7.4$

2. $a_1 = 0.3$; $d = 1.4$; these give: $a_2 = 1.7$; $a_3 = 3.1$; $a_4 = 4.5$

Geometric sequences:

1. $a_1 = 5$; $q = 2$; these give: $a_2 = 10$; $a_3 = 20$; $a_4 = 40$

2. $a_1 = 16$; $q = 1.5$; these give: $a_2 = 24$; $a_3 = 36$; $a_4 = 54$

2. Computing the *n*-th term from the initial conditions

To obtain a given term of a sequence, it is tedious to calculate all of the sequence terms up to that point; therefore, we seek an explicit formula for the *n*-th term of the sequence.

For an arithmetic sequence, we have:

$$a_2 = a_1 + d$$
$$a_3 = a_2 + d = a_1 + d + d = a_1 + 2 \cdot d$$
$$a_4 = a_3 + d = a_1 + 2 \cdot d + d = a_1 + 3 \cdot d$$

generally,

$$a_n = a_1 + (n-1) \cdot d.$$

The *n*-th term of an arithmetic sequence is calculated by adding $(n-1)$ times the growth amount d to the first term.

Examples:

1. Mr. Maurer's wage in the 16th year amounts to
$\$23.00 + (16-1) \cdot \$1.50 = \$23.00 + 15 \cdot \$\,1.50 = \$\,45.50$

2. $a_1 = 5$; $d = 0.8$;
$a_4 = 5 + 3 \cdot 0.8 = 5 + 2.4 = 7.4$;
$a_{10} = 5 + 9 \cdot 0.8 = 5 + 7.2 = 12.2$;

3. It can also happen that the terms of the sequence always decrease by a fixed amount – i.e., the growth amount d is negative:
$a_1 = 15$; $a_2 = 12$; $a_3 = 9$; here we have $d = -3$.
The 10th term is thus
$a_{10} = 15 - 3 \cdot 9 = 15 - 27 = -12$.

For geometric sequences we have:

$$a_2 = a_1 \cdot q$$
$$a_3 = a_2 \cdot q = a_1 \cdot q \cdot q = a_1 \cdot q^2$$
$$a_4 = a_3 \cdot q = a_1 \cdot q^2 \cdot q = a_1 \cdot q^3$$

generally

$$a_n = a_1 \cdot q^{n-1}.$$

The *n*-th term of a geometric sequence can be calculated from the first term by multiplying by the $(n-1)$-st power of the growth factor q.

Examples:

1. Mr. Drechsler's wage in the 16th year amounts to
   $\$23.00 \cdot 1.05^{16-1} = \$23.00 \cdot 1.05^{15} = \$ 47.8153 \approx \$ 47.82$.
   (The discrepancy in table in I.1 is due to the fact that amounts were rounded there to the nearest cent).

2. $a_1 = 5; q = 2;$
   $a_2 = 10;$
   $a_3 = 5 \cdot 2^2 = 5 \cdot 4 = 20;$
   $a_4 = 5 \cdot 2^3 = 5 \cdot 8 = 40.$

3. $a_1 = 16; q = 1.5;$
   $a_2 = 16 \cdot 1.5 = 24;$
   $a_3 = 16 \cdot 1.5^2 = 16 \cdot 2.25 = 36;$
   $a_4 = 16 \cdot 1.5^3 = 16 \cdot 3.375 = 54;$
   $a_{10} = 16 \cdot 1.5^9 = 615.09375.$

4. It can also happen that the terms of a sequence are always diminished by a constant factor, i.e., the factor q is less than 1:
   $a_1 = 16; a_2 = 8; a_3 = 4;$ here we have $q = \frac{1}{2}.$
   We find that $a_6 = 16 \cdot \left(\frac{1}{2}\right)^5 = 16 \cdot \frac{1}{32} = \frac{1}{2}.$

5. If q is negative in a geometric sequence, then the following curiosity arises:
   $a_1 = 3; q = -2;$
   Then we have $a_2 = 3 \cdot (-2) = -6;$
   $a_3 = 3 \cdot (-2)^2 = 3 \cdot 4 = 12;$
   $a_4 = 12 \cdot (-2) = -24.$
   The signs of the terms changes constantly. Such a sequence is called an alternating sequence.

Two further examples:

1. At a depth of 25 m the temperature equals the median annual temperature for that location, and for each additional 32 m depth, there is an increase of 1°C (1 Kelvin).

   a) What temperature would there be in an unventilated coal mine at a depth of 980 m if the median annual temperature were 11°C?

   b) At what depth would the temperature reach the maximum allowed for miners, namely 28°C?

2. The average air pressure at sea level is about 1016 hPa (hectoPascal = millibar = mbar). Each increase of 80 m in altitude drops the air pressure 1%.

   a) How high is the average air pressure on the Piz Mundaun at an altitude of 2064m?

   b) At what altitude is there a place whose median air pressure is 960 hPa?

Solution:

1. a) How many 32 m-steps is the 980 m mine below the level of 25 m?
    Here $a_1 = 25$ m; $d = 32$ m.

    $$980\,\mathrm{m} = 25\,\mathrm{m} + x \cdot 32\,\mathrm{m}$$
    $$955\,\mathrm{m} = x \cdot 32\,\mathrm{m}$$
    $$x = \frac{955}{32} = 29.84375 \approx 30.$$

    That means, at a depth of 980 m, the temperature is 30°C more than at the surface. So that amounts to 41°C. Only by constant ventilation of cool fresh air from the surface is it possible to bring the temperature down to 28°C.

    b) Here we must ask ourselves: how many 32 m-steps can we go below the level of 25 m? Apparently it can be 28°C − 11°C = 17°C warmer than at the depth of 25 m. The answer we seek, then, is the 18th term of an arithmetic sequence.

    $$a_{18} = 25\,\mathrm{m} + 17 \cdot 32\,\mathrm{m} = 569\,\mathrm{m}$$

    The temperature of 28°C is reached at a depth of 569 m.

2. a) The air pressure decreases by 1 % with each increase of 80 m in altitude, i.e., if one climbs to 80 m, then it amounts to only 99 % of its measured value below. Recall that $99\% = \frac{99}{100} = 0.99$. Here we have $a_1 = 1016$; $q = 0.99$. How many 80 m-steps are there from sea level to the Piz Mundaun?
    $2064 : 80 = 25.8 \approx 26$. The answer we seek, then, is the 27th term of a geometric sequence:

    $$a_{27} = a_1 \cdot q^{26} = 1016\,\mathrm{hPa} \cdot 0.99^{26}$$
    $$= 782.4\,\mathrm{hPa} \approx 782\,\mathrm{hPa}$$

    The air pressure on the Mundaun amounts on average to about 782 hPa (that means that water boils at just 92°C!).

    b) How many times must we multiply 1016 by 0.99 in order to reach 960? If we could solve the equation $960 = 1016 \cdot 0.99^x$, then $x \cdot 80$ m would be the desired altitude above sea level at the desired location. With the above means this problem can only be solved by trial and error. A true solution will have to be postponed until the end of the lesson block (III.3).

3. The Sum Formulas

Recall the problem from I.1, where we were asked about the annually increasing wages of Mr. Maurer and Mr. Drechsler. With that, we also sought the sum of the first n terms of a sequence. It would be useful if we could calculate such sums from the initial terms and the growth amount or the growth factor. For an arithmetic sequence, we have:

$$a_1 + a_2 + .. + a_n = n \cdot \frac{a_1 + a_n}{2}$$

$$= n \cdot \frac{1}{2} \cdot (a_1 + a_1 + (n-1) \cdot d)$$

$$= n \left(a_1 + \frac{n-1}{2} \cdot d \right) = s_n$$

Example: Suppose you decide to put a little something into savings each week, and you begin with $5, increasing this amount each week by 20 cents. How much have you saved after 2 years?

Solution:

$a_1 = 5; d = 0.2$; last term $= a_{104}$; sum is

$$a_1 + a_2 + ... + a_{104} = 104 \cdot \left(5 + \frac{103}{2} \cdot 0.2 \right)$$

$$= 104 \cdot (5 + 10.3)$$

$$= 104 \cdot 15.3$$

$$= 1591.20$$

You've saved $1591.20.

With geometric sequences one can find the following sum formula:

$$s_n = a_1 \cdot \frac{q^n - 1}{q - 1} = a_1 \cdot \frac{1 - q^n}{1 - q}$$

(The derivation and proof of this formula will be given in a later lesson block).

We "test" the formula with a few examples:

1. When $a_1 = 3; q = 2$

$$a_1 + a_2 + a_3 + a_4 = 3 \cdot \frac{2^4 - 1}{2 - 1} = 3 \cdot \frac{15}{1} = 45$$

Check: $3 + 6 + 12 + 24 = 45$

2. When $a_1 = 5; q = -3$

$$a_1 + a_2 + a_3 + a_4 + a_5 = 5 \cdot \frac{1 - (-3)^5}{1 - (-3)}$$

$$= 5 \cdot \frac{1 + 243}{4} = 5 \cdot 61$$

$$= 305$$

Check: $5 - 15 + 45 - 135 + 405 = 305$

For the sum $a_1 + a_2 + a_3 + a_4 + \dots + a_n$, one can abbreviate as follows:

$$\sum_{i=1}^{n} a_i.$$

Read: "sum over all a_i, i equals 1 to n"

Application:

Suppose $a_1 = 2$; $q = 5$; we seek the sum of the first 6 terms, as well as the sum of the 4th through 7th terms.

$$\sum_{i=1}^{6} a_i = 2 \cdot \frac{5^6 - 1}{5 - 1} = \frac{15,624}{4} \cdot 2 = 7,812$$

$$\sum_{i=1}^{7} a_i = \sum_{i=1}^{7} a_i - \sum_{i=1}^{3}$$
$$= 2 \cdot \frac{78,124}{4} - 2 \cdot \frac{124}{4}$$
$$= 39,062 - 62$$
$$= 39,000$$

Check: $250 + 1,250 + 6,250 + 31,250 = 39,000$.

4. Harmonic Sequences

From the physics block in the 6th grade, we are familiar with the basic ratios of the naturally occurring overtone sequence. The actual overtones of a vibrating string oscillate with the half, third, fourth, etc. of the string length; the distances from node to node in the associated wave, when the entire string length is used as the unit 1, form a sequence of the form

$$1; \ \frac{1}{2}; \ \frac{1}{3}; \ \frac{1}{4}; \ \frac{1}{5}; \ \frac{1}{6}; \dots$$

Such a sequence is therefore called a *harmonic sequence*.

One quickly recognizes: the reciprocals of the terms of a harmonic sequence form an arithmetic sequence; conversely, the reciprocals of an arithmetic sequence form a harmonic sequence.

Examples: In addition to the "classical" harmonic sequence

$$a_n = \frac{1}{n} \quad \text{with } n \in \mathbb{N}^*$$

the reciprocals of other arithmetic sequences also form harmonic sequences:

$$\frac{2}{3}; \ \frac{2}{5}; \ \frac{2}{7}; \ \frac{2}{9}; \ \frac{2}{11}; \ \frac{2}{13}; \dots$$

$$\frac{5}{3}; \ 1; \ \frac{5}{7}; \ \frac{5}{9}; \ \frac{5}{11}; \ \frac{5}{13}; \ \frac{1}{3}; \dots$$

5. The Means

What is the mean of 3 and 12? If we consider the arithmetic sequence 3; 7.5; 12; 16.5; ..., then it becomes clear that we could consider 7.5 to be the mean between 3 and 12. On the other hand, if we take the geometric sequence 3; 6; 12; 24 ..., then we must regard 6 as the mean value between 3 and 12.

Finally one could also think of a harmonic sequence with the terms

$$\frac{12}{4} = 3; \ \frac{12}{2.5} = 4.8; \ \frac{12}{1} = 12; \ \frac{12}{-0.5} = -24; \ ...$$

so that 4.8 could also be considered the mean value between 3 and 12.

The median value: $m(a, b)$ is thus the middle of three terms of a sequence, where a and b are the other two terms. Associated with each of the three types of sequences we have studied, we distinguish three kinds of mean values:

The *arithmetic mean* of two numbers a and b (abbreviated: $m_a(a, b)$) has the same difference to a and b; so it holds that: $m - a = b - m$. From this it follows: $2m = a + b$, or

$$m_a(a, b) = \frac{a+b}{2}.$$

The *geometric mean* of two numbers a and b (abbreviated: $m_g(a, b)$) forms, with a and b, the same quotient; so it holds that: $\frac{m}{a} = \frac{b}{m}$. From this it follows: $m^2 = a \cdot b$, or

$$m_g(a, b) = \sqrt{a \cdot b}.$$

(Naturally $m_g(a, b) = -\sqrt{a \cdot b}$ is also a solution of this equation. Indeed this would also be a mean value in the above sense of the word – it belongs to an alternating sequence. To avoid unnecessary confusion, however, it is best to keep this limited to a brief mention – depending on the class, perhaps not even this, unless a student inquires).

With the *harmonic mean* of two numbers a and b (abbreviated: $m_h(a, b)$), the reciprocal of the mean value is the arithmetic mean of the reciprocals of a and b; thus it holds that: $\frac{1}{m} = \frac{\frac{1}{a}+\frac{1}{b}}{2}$

From this it follows that:

$$\frac{1}{m} = \frac{\frac{1}{a} + \frac{1}{b}}{2} = \frac{\frac{a+b}{a \cdot b}}{2} = \frac{a+b}{2 \cdot a \cdot b},$$

thus

$$m_h(a, b) = \frac{2 \cdot a \cdot b}{a+b}.$$

Remark: All three mean values can be visualized geometrically, that is, as segment lengths that can be constructed from two given lengths. For more information, please refer to the article *Georg Glöckler*: Rekursives Rechnen.

Examples:

1. A water basin is filled by first emptying the contents of an 8 liter jar into it, then a 4 liter jar. What size jar would be needed to fill the basin exactly by emptying its contents twice? The jar must have the same amount less than 8 liters as it has more than 4 liters. It is therefore the arithmetic mean that we seek. $m = (8L + 4L : 2 = 6L$. The jar must therefore hold 6 liters.

2. A field measures 50 m wide by 200 m long. What is the length of a side of a square field that has the same area? The area of the field amounts to $50\,\text{m} \cdot 200\,\text{m} = 10{,}000\,\text{m}^2$; but a square that has an area of $10{,}000\,\text{m}^2$ has a side of length $\sqrt{10{,}000\,\text{m}^2} = 100\,\text{m}$.

Here the notion of "geometric mean" becomes apparent: the geometric mean of two segments a and b is the length of the side of a square that has the same area as a rectangle with sides a and b.

3. A chain smoker who smokes 60 cigarettes a day would like to quit smoking. In doing so, he'd like to cut back to 10 cigarettes per day in 5 weeks – and because he cut his consumption in half the first week, he continued accordingly, and in the fifth week he was down to a sixth – 10 cigarettes – of the original amount. What number must he cut back to in the middle (the third) week?
   The sequence here is

   $$\frac{60}{2}; \frac{60}{3}; \frac{60}{4}; \frac{60}{5}; \frac{60}{6}; \dots$$

   so in the middle week we have an amount of 15 cigarettes. Indeed it also holds that

   $$m_g(30,\ 10) = \frac{2 \cdot 30 \cdot 10}{30 + 10} = \frac{600}{40} = 15$$

Remark:
Whenever the arithmetic, geometric, and harmonic means are formed from a given pair of numbers, then not only does the geometric mean assume a value in between the other two; it is in fact the geometric mean of the other two means:

$$m_g(m_a,\ m_h) = \sqrt{\frac{a+b}{2} \cdot \frac{2ab}{a+b}} = \sqrt{ab}.$$

II. Calculating Powers and Roots

1. The n-th power

Recall from earlier:

$$a + a + a + a + a + a + a = 7 \cdot a$$

that repeated addition can be abbreviated by multiplication.

Similarly, we can also abbreviate repeated multiplication:

$$a \cdot a \cdot a \cdot a \cdot a \cdot a \cdot a \cdot a \cdot a = a^9$$

or generally:

$$\underbrace{a \cdot a \cdot a \cdot \ldots \cdot a}_{n-\text{times}} = a^n.$$

From this, one can recognize several rules that emerge:

1. $a^3 \cdot a^2 = a \cdot a \cdot a \cdot a \cdot a = a^5 \,(= a^{3+2})$ or generally:

$$\underbrace{a \cdot a \cdot a \cdot \ldots \cdot a}_{n-\text{times}} \cdot \underbrace{a \cdot a \cdot a \cdot \ldots \cdot a}_{m-\text{times}} = a^{n+m}.$$

2. $\frac{a^6}{a^4} = \frac{a \cdot a \cdot a \cdot a \cdot a \cdot a}{a \cdot a \cdot a \cdot a} = a^2 \,(= a^{6-4})$ or generally:

$$\frac{a^n}{a^m} = a^{n-m},$$

(at first with the restriction that $n > m$).

Notation:

$$\text{exponent} \searrow$$
$$a^n \;\}\text{power}$$
$$\text{base} \nearrow$$

We call this operation exponentiation (compare with addition, division, etc.)

Examples:

1. $x^2 \cdot x^3 = x^5$

2. $2^3 \cdot 2^7 = 2^{10} = 1024$

3. $\left(a^2 + a^3\right)^2 = a^4 + 2a^5 + a^6 = a^4\left(1 + 2a + a^2\right)$

4. $\frac{27a^3 \cdot \left(7b^2\right)^5}{21^3 \cdot \left(ab^3\right)^3} = 49b$

2. The *n*-th Root

We recognize division as the inverse of multiplication:

$$3 \cdot 5 = 15$$
$$15 : 3 = 5$$

accordingly, we can find an inverse of squaring:

$$7^2 = 49$$
$$\sqrt{49} = 7$$

or generally:

$$\sqrt{a^2} = a.$$

In an entirely similar manner, we can define "higher roots" as the inverses of higher powers:

$$3^3 = 27$$
$$\sqrt[3]{27} = 3$$
$$5^4 = 625$$
$$\sqrt[4]{625} = 5$$

or generally:

The *n*-th root of a number *a* is that positive number *b* whose *n*-th power is *a*.

Examples:

$\sqrt[4]{81} = 3;\ \sqrt[3]{8} = 2;\ \sqrt[4]{4} = \sqrt[2]{2} = \sqrt{2};$ (the usual root – square root – without a "root exponent" is therefore the 2nd root).

$$\sqrt{r^6} = r^3 \ (\text{since } r^3 \cdot r^3 = r^6)$$
$$\sqrt[3]{r^6} = r^2 \ (\text{since } r^2 \cdot r^2 \cdot r^2 = r^6).$$

Notation[3]:

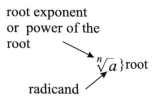

root exponent
or power of the
root

$\sqrt[n]{a}\,\}$root

radicand

We call this operation root extraction. It is not always possible to pull every number and variable "evenly" out of a root. However, when there is a *product*, the root can be extracted from each of the individual factors: for example,

$$\sqrt{144} = \sqrt{16} \cdot \sqrt{9} = 4 \cdot 3 = 12.$$

So it is possible, in certain cases, to extract roots in a piecewise manner. Examples:

$$\sqrt{8} = \sqrt{4 \cdot 2} = 2 \cdot \sqrt{2}$$
$$\sqrt{147} = \sqrt{49 \cdot 3} = 7 \cdot \sqrt{3}$$
$$\sqrt{12a^2b^3} = \sqrt{4 \cdot 3 \cdot a^2 \cdot b^2 \cdot b} = 2ab \cdot \sqrt{3b}$$

---

[3] Helpful to remember: *radicand*– the number under the radical; *dividend* – the number under the division symbol

3. The Four Laws of Exponents

All the operations we know up to this point (and their inverses) can be arranged into a hierarchy according to their relative strength:

$$3. \quad \uparrow \qquad \sqrt{}$$

$$2. \quad \cdot \qquad :$$

$$1. \quad + \qquad -$$

Some operations can be carried out just as well in the base as in the exponents. For example, the following holds:

1. $2^3 \cdot 2^4 = 2 \cdot 2 \cdot 2 \cdot 2 \cdot 2 \cdot 2 \cdot 2 = 2^{3+4} = 2^7$

2. $3^5 : 3^3 = \frac{3 \cdot 3 \cdot 3 \cdot 3 \cdot 3}{3 \cdot 3 \cdot 3} = 3^{5-3} = 3^2$

3. $\left(5^2\right)^3 = 5^2 \cdot 5^2 \cdot 5^2 = 5^{3 \cdot 2} = 5^6$

4. $\sqrt[4]{3^8} = 3^2$ since $\left(3^2\right)^4 = 3^{2 \cdot 4} = 3^8$

Generally:

If we carry an operation over from the level of the base to the level of the exponents, then we must descend one level in the hierarchy of operations, and the same holds in the other direction. In this way, we obtain the four laws of exponents that were illustrated in the examples above:

1. If two powers with the same base are multiplied, then the base is retained and the exponents are added:
$$a^r \cdot a^s = a^{r+s}.$$

2. If two powers with the same base are divided, then the base is retained and the exponents are subtracted:
$$a^r : a^s = \frac{a^r}{a^s} = a^{r-s}.$$

3. If a power is exponentiated, then the exponents are multiplied:
$$\left(a^s\right)^r = a^{s \cdot r}.$$

4. If a root is extracted from a power, then the exponents are divided:
$$\sqrt[s]{a^r} = a^{r:s} = a^{\frac{r}{s}}.$$

Examples:

1. a) $7^7 \cdot 7^9 = 7^{11}$;   b) $q^{17} \cdot q^3 = q^{20}$

2. a) $5^8 : 5^3 = 5^5$ b) $r^{12} : r^2 = r^{10}$ c) $2^n : 2 = 2^{n-1}$ d) $\frac{3^{2r}}{3^3} = 3^{2r-3}$

3. a) $\left(3^2\right)^3 = 3^6$ b) $\left(5^r\right)^3 = 5^{3r}$ c) $\left(b^3\right)^q = b^{3q}$ d) $\left(e^x\right)^2 = e^{2x}$

4. a) $\sqrt[3]{216} = \sqrt[3]{6^3} = 6$ b) $\sqrt[4]{2^8} = 2^2 = 4$ c) $\sqrt[5]{s^{15}} = s^3$ d) $\sqrt[r]{a^{12}} = r^{\frac{12}{r}}$

Generally it holds that powers and roots with the same exponents cancel each other out:

$$\left(\sqrt[n]{a}\right)^n = a; \quad \sqrt[n]{a^n} = a$$

4. Powers and Roots of Products and Fractions

From our work with the binomial theorem, we know that $(a+b)^2$ is not $a^2 + b^2$. Expanding powers of sums (and differences) is therefore a relatively tedious process; so, for example,

$$(a+b)^4 = a^4 + 4a^3b + 6a^2b^2 + 4ab^3 + b^4$$

In contrast, the powers of products are much easier: it holds, namely, that

$$(a \cdot b)^3 = (a \cdot b) \cdot (a \cdot b) \cdot (a \cdot b) = a \cdot b \cdot a \cdot b \cdot a \cdot b = a^3 b^3$$

or generally:

$$(a \cdot b)^n = a^n \cdot b^n$$

If a product is exponentiated, then the factors can be exponentiated individually. The corresponding rule holds for fractions:

$$\left(\frac{a}{b}\right)^n = \frac{a^n}{b^n}.$$

If a fraction is exponentiated, then the numerator and denominator can be exponentiated separately.

The same holds for roots:

$$\sqrt[3]{125a^3} = \sqrt[3]{125} \cdot \sqrt[3]{a^3} = 5a$$

$$\sqrt[4]{\frac{a^{12}}{b^{16}}} = \frac{a^3}{b^4}.$$

In a product, the roots of the individual factors can be extracted separately; in a fraction, the roots of the numerator and denominator can be extracted separately.

5. Generalizing the Concept of Powers

We observe the following sequence of problems:

$$2^4 : 2^2 = 2^{2-2} = 4$$

$$2^4 : 2^3 = 2^1 = 2$$

$$2^4 : 2^4 = \frac{2^4}{2^4} = \frac{2 \cdot 2 \cdot 2 \cdot 2}{2 \cdot 2 \cdot 2 \cdot 2} = 1$$

It also holds that

$$2^4 : 2^4 = 2^{4-4} = 2^0, \text{ and therefore } 2^0 = 1.$$

It holds that

$$2^4 : 2^5 = \frac{2 \cdot 2 \cdot 2 \cdot 2}{2 \cdot 2 \cdot 2 \cdot 2 \cdot 2} = \frac{1}{2},$$

but also that

$$2^4 : 2^5 = 2^{4-5} = 2^{-1}, \text{ and therefore } 2^{-1} = \frac{1}{2}.$$

It holds that

$$2^4 : 2^6 = \frac{2^4}{2^6} = \frac{2 \cdot 2 \cdot 2 \cdot 2}{2 \cdot 2 \cdot 2 \cdot 2 \cdot 2 \cdot 2} = \frac{1}{2^2} = \frac{1}{4}$$

but also that

$$2^4 : 2^6 = 2^{4-6} = 2^{-2}, \text{ therefore } 2^{-2} = \frac{1}{2^2} = \frac{1}{4}.$$

A reasonable extension of the operation of exponentiation to include the exponent 0 and negative exponents can thus only be:

$$a^{-n} = \frac{1}{a^n}.$$

A negative exponent thus signifies the reciprocal of the number with the positive exponent. In particular, we have:

$$a^{-1} = \frac{1}{a^1} = \frac{1}{a}; \quad \left(\frac{a}{b}\right)^{-1} = \frac{b}{a}; \quad a^0 = 1.$$

This holds for all real numbers except 0! ($a \in \mathbb{R}^*$).

Additionally, we consider the following sequence:

$$\sqrt[2]{64} = \sqrt[2]{2^6} = 2^{6:2} = 2^3 = 8$$

$$\sqrt[3]{64} = \sqrt[3]{2^6} = 2^{6:3} = 2^2 = 4$$

$$\sqrt[n]{a^r} = a^{r:n}$$

$$\sqrt[n]{a} = \sqrt[n]{a^1} = a^{1:n} = a^{\frac{1}{n}}.$$

It thus holds generally: the n-th root of a can also be written as

$$\sqrt[n]{a} = a^{\frac{1}{n}}.$$

Examples:

1. $\left(\sqrt{5}\right)^3 = 5^{\frac{1}{2} \cdot 3} = 5^{\frac{3}{2}} = 5^{1.5} = 5^{1+\frac{1}{2}} = 5 \cdot \sqrt{5}$

2. $\sqrt[5]{q^{17}} = q^{\frac{17}{5}}$

3. $\frac{a^2 b^3 c^4}{a^4 b^3 c^2} = a^{-2} \cdot c^2$

4. $123,000 = 1.23 \cdot 10^5$

5. $0.00321 = \frac{3.21}{1000} = \frac{3.21}{10^3} = 3.21 \cdot 10^{-3}$

Notice:

$1,000 = 10^3$; $100 = 10^2$; $10 = 10^1$; $1 = 10^0$; $0.1 = 10^{-1}$; $0.01 = 10^{-2}$; $0.001 = 10^{-3}$.

We can also use not only natural numbers as exponents, but indeed it also makes sense to use any real number.

III. The Logarithm

1. Introduction

All the operations we know up to this point can be inverted in two different ways:

Addition

$$3 + 7 = 10$$

"I have 3, and I receive 7 more – how many do I have now?"

Inverses:

$10 = 3 + x$	$10 = x + 7$
$10 - 3 = 7$	$10 - 7 = 3$

"In total, I now have 10; I originally had 3 – how many more did I receive?"

"In total, I now have 10; I had received 7 more to my original amount – how many did I have to begin with?"

Multiplication

$$5 \cdot \$6 = \$30$$

"I have 5 times \$6 – how much do I have in all?"

Inverses:

$\$30 = 5 \cdot \$x$	$\$30 = x \cdot \$6$
$\$30 : 5 = \$6$	$\$30 : \$6 = 5$

"I distribute \$30 among 5 people – how much does each get?"

"I have \$30 – how many tickets at \$6 apiece can I buy?"

"Dividing"

"Measuring"

Exponentiation

$$5^3 = 125$$

"I multiply the number 5 by itself 3 times – what do I get?"

Inverses:

$$x^3 = 125$$
$$\sqrt[3]{125} = 5$$

$$5^x = 125$$
$$\log_5 125 = 3$$

"What number do I have to multiply by itself 3 times to obtain 125?"

So here a root (in this case a cube root) is being sought.

"How many times must I multiply 5 by itself to obtain 125?"

Here an exponent is sought whose application to a given base leads to a particular result.

By the logarithm of a number a to the base b we mean that number c to which we must raise b to obtain a:

$$\log_b a = c \iff b^c = a$$

Examples:

1. $\log_2 8 = 3$ (since $2^3 = 8$)

2. $\log_3 81 = 4$

3. $\log_{10} 1,000 = 3$

4. $\log_{10} 1,000,000 = 6$

5. $\log_{10} 0.1 = -1$

6. $\log_{10} 0.01 = -2$

Most commonly, logarithms are chosen that use a base of 2, 10, or e (e is Euler's constant $e \approx 2.718$; more about this later).

Notation:

$\log_e$ denotes the natural logarithm, abbrv.: ln;
$\log_{10}$ denotes the decimal logarithm, abbrv.: lg.

Examples:

1. $\lg 0.25 \approx -0.602$

2. $\lg 400 \approx 2.602$

3. $\ln 15 \approx 2.708$

4. $\ln \pi \approx 1.145$

2. The Four Laws of Logarithms

Through a careful comparison with the four laws of exponents, we can easily find the correspond-ing rules of logarithms:

1. Law of exponents: $125 \cdot 25 = 5^3 \cdot 5^2 = 5^{3+2} = 5^5$ consequently:

$$\log_5 (125 \cdot 5) = \log_5 125 + \log_5 25 = 3 + 2 = 5.$$

The logarithm of a product equals the sum of the logarithms of the individual factors.

$$\log_a (b \cdot c) = \log_a b + \log_a c.$$

2. Law of exponents: $729 : 9 = 3^6 : 3^2 = 3^{6-2} = 3^4$ consequently:

$$\log_3 \left(\frac{729}{9} \right) = \log_3 (729 : 9)$$

$$= \log_3 729 - \log_3 9 = 6 - 2 = 4.$$

The logarithm of a fraction (or quotient) equals the difference of the logarithms of the numerator and denominator:

$$\log_a (b : c) = \log_a b - \log_a c.$$

3. Law of exponents: $36^3 = \left(6^2 \right)^3 = 6^{2 \cdot 3} = 6^6$ consequently:

$$\log_6 \left(36^3 \right) = 3 \cdot \log_6 36 = 3 \cdot 2 = 6.$$

To obtain the logarithm of a power, the logarithm of the base is multiplied by the exponent:

$$\log_a \left(b^c \right) = c \cdot \log_a b.$$

4. Law of exponents: $\sqrt[2]{81} = \sqrt[2]{3^4} = 3^{\frac{4}{2}} = 3^2$ consequently:

$$\log_3 \left(\sqrt[2]{81} \right) = \frac{\log_3 81}{2} = \frac{\log_3 3^4}{2} = \frac{4}{2} = 2.$$

To obtain the logarithm of a root, the logarithm of the radicand is divided by the root exponent:

$$\log_a \left(\sqrt[c]{b} \right) = \frac{\log_a b}{c}.$$

Examples:

1. $\log_2 \left(1024^5 \right) = 5 \cdot \log_2 1024 = 5 \cdot 10 = 50$
2. $\lg \left(5.31 \cdot 10^{23} \right) = \lg (5.31) + \lg \left(10^{23} \right) \approx 0.72509452 + 23 = 23.72509452$
3. $\ln \left(\sqrt[6]{e} \right) = \frac{\ln e}{6} = \frac{1}{6}$

3. Calculating General Logarithms

The calculator only gives us logarithms with the bases 10 and e. In order to be able to calculate logarithms with other bases, we observe the following:

$$\log_a b = x$$
$$a^x = b$$
$$\ln (a^x) = \ln b$$
$$x \cdot \ln a = \ln b$$
$$x = \frac{\ln b}{\ln a}.$$

So it holds that:

$$\log_a b = \frac{\ln b}{\ln a}.$$

We check this:

$$\log_2 512 = \frac{\ln 512}{\ln 2} \approx 6.238324625 : 0.69314718 = 9.$$

(This is accurate to eight decimal places. In place of the natural logarithm (ln), we could use the base 10 (lg), or any other known logarithm.)

We can now calculate logarithms with any positive base but 1:

Examples:

1. $\log_6 57 \approx 2.256469876$

2. $\log_{1.5} 2.25 \approx 0.810930216 : 0.4054651089 = 2.$

4. Solving Exponential Equations

An equation of the form $a^x = b$, in which the exponent is sought, is called an exponential equation. In order to solve it, a logarithm with base a must be applied to both sides of the equation:

$$a^x = b$$
$$x = \log_a b$$

Now we possess the means to solve the air pressure problem from section I.2:

$$960\,\text{hPa} = 1016\,\text{hPa} \cdot 0.99^x$$
$$960\,\text{hPa} : 1016\,\text{hPa} = 0.99^x$$
$$\log_{0.99} \left(\frac{960}{1016} \right) = x$$
$$x = \frac{\lg \left(\frac{960}{1016} \right)}{\lg 0.99}$$
$$= 5.641$$

An air pressure of 960 hPa is thus reached after 5.641 steps of 80 meters; that means at an altitude of 451 m above sea level.

A further example:
What is the doubling time of an investment that has an annual interest rate of 3.25 % ?

After each year, the account balance is increased by $3,25\%$ of the previous balance. So we obtain

$$100\% + 3.25\% = 103.25\%,$$

that is, a multiple of 1.0325 (times the previous balance).
It needs to be determined how many times the factor 1.0325 must be applied before a doubling of the original amount is achieved (the factor 2 is reached). Therefore:

$$1.0325^x = 2$$
$$x = \log_{1.0325} 2$$
$$x \approx 21.67.$$

So it takes about 21 years and 8 months until the principal amount has doubled.

IV. Approximation Techniques

Many computations cannot be accomplished exactly via the basic operations; and in practice, an approximate value is often sufficient. A variety of techniques for calculating approximations are based on repeated calculations (recursive computations) that get successively closer to the desired quantity.

1. Newton's Method

Isaac Newton developed a very practical technique for calculating square roots[4], in which one uses a recursive formula to approach the root as closely as desired.

We seek the value of $\sqrt{x}$. We set:

$$a_0 = \frac{x}{2}; \ a_{n+1} = \frac{a_n^2 + x}{2a_n}$$

The term a_{n+1} is recursively computed from the term a_n. Example:

Suppose we want to find $\sqrt{5}$.

$$a_0 = 2.5$$
$$a_1 = \frac{2.5^2 + 5}{2 \cdot 2.5} = \frac{6.25 + 5}{5} = 2.25$$
$$a_2 = \frac{2.25^2 + 5}{2 \cdot 2.25} = 2.23611$$

---

[4]The method is also described by other mathematicians and is known in a slightly different forms, for example the Bombelli-method. See the article by Baum in *Mathematical Topics for the 9th Grade*, "Irrationality in Arithmetic and Geometry and the Extraction of Roots"

This is already a very good approximation to $\sqrt{5} \approx 2.236067$.

This method has two major advantages:

1. It converges very quickly; that is, a small number of steps suffice to reach a very high precision.

2. It is self-correcting; that is, if an error is introduced, it will automatically be corrected in subsequent steps.

The process is thus extremely powerful – more powerful than the initial conditions!

Example:
Suppose we want to find $\sqrt{17}$.

1. We begin with 10:

$$a_1 = 10$$
$$a_2 = \frac{10^2 + 17}{20} = 5.85$$
$$a_3 = \frac{5.85^2 + 17}{11.7} = 4.378$$
$$a_4 = \frac{4.378^2 + 17}{8.756} = 4.131$$
$$a_5 = \frac{4.131^2 + 17}{8.262} = 4.1231$$

We begin with 3:

$$a_1 = 3$$
$$a_2 = \frac{3^2 + 17}{6} = 4.\overline{33}$$
$$a_3 = \frac{4.\overline{33}^2 + 17}{8.\overline{66}} = 4.1282$$
$$a_4 = \frac{4.1282^2 + 17}{8.2564} = 4.1231$$

So this method provides us with approximations for roots in *decimal notation*.

2. Continued Fractions

Often it is the case that desired quantities can be approximated by relatively simple fractions; for example, $\frac{17}{20}$ is a good approximation to $\frac{113}{133}$.

Such approximations (arbitrarily precise ratios) can be obtained through the stepwise development of a fraction that is improper to a large degree (the denominator contains fractions within fractions).

Examples:

1. Suppose we seek a simple fraction approximating $\frac{113}{133}$

We have:

$$\frac{113}{133} = \frac{1}{\frac{133}{113}} = \frac{1}{1 + \frac{20}{113}} = \frac{1}{1 + \frac{1}{\frac{113}{20}}} = \frac{1}{1 + \frac{1}{5 + \frac{13}{20}}}$$

$$= \frac{1}{1 + \frac{1}{5 + \frac{1}{\frac{20}{13}}}} = \frac{1}{1 + \frac{1}{5 + \frac{1}{1 + \frac{7}{13}}}} \approx \frac{1}{1 + \frac{1}{5 + \frac{1}{1 + \frac{1}{2}}}}$$

Monstrous fraction expressions like these are called continued fractions; the repeated taking of reciprocals serves a purpose, namely, to extract whole numbers out of the fraction and thereby to arrive at increasingly smaller numbers.

A completed continued fraction has only the number 1 in its numerators.

The final approximate fraction (where $\frac{7}{13}$ was approximated by $\frac{1}{2}$) leads us back all the way to a standard fraction:

$$\frac{1}{1 + \frac{1}{5 + \frac{1}{1 + \frac{1}{2}}}} = \frac{1}{1 + \frac{1}{5 + \frac{1}{\frac{3}{2}}}} = \frac{1}{1 + \frac{1}{5 + \frac{2}{3}}} = \frac{1}{1 + \frac{1}{\frac{17}{3}}}$$

$$= \frac{1}{1 + \frac{3}{17}} = \frac{1}{\frac{20}{17}} = \frac{17}{20}.$$

So we have that $\frac{17}{20}$ is a good approximation for $\frac{113}{133}$. Indeed,

$$\frac{113}{133} : \frac{17}{20} = 0.99956$$

which means that the error is less than 0.05%.

2. The Saros-Cycle for Solar Eclipses[5]

The elapsed time between successive new moons averages 29.5306 days (*synodical* month); the plane containing the orbit of the moon is slightly tilted with respect to the plane containing the orbit of the earth around the sun, and 27.2122 days elapse between successive instants when the moon passes through this plane in a given direction (*draconitic* month).

In order for a solar eclipse to take place, the sun, moon, and earth must lie in a straight line. This configuration will repeat (approximately) when after a whole number of synodical months have passed, a whole number of draconitic months have also simultaneously been completed; that means a whole number multiple of 29.5306 (days) must equal a whole number multiple of

---

[5]This example is treated thoroughly in the previously mentioned article by P. Baum in *Mathematical Topics for the 9th Grade*.

27.2122 (days). We therefore seek a rational approximation to $295,306 : 272,122$. We have that

$$\frac{295,306}{272,122} = \frac{147,653}{136,061} = 1 + \frac{11,592}{136,061}$$

$$= 1 + \frac{1}{\frac{136,061}{11,592}} = 1 + \frac{1}{11 + \frac{8,549}{11,592}}$$

$$= 1 + \frac{1}{11 + \frac{1}{\frac{11,592}{8549}}} = 1 + \frac{1}{11 + \frac{1}{1 + \frac{3043}{8549}}}$$

$$= 1 + \frac{1}{11 + \frac{1}{1 + \frac{1}{\frac{8549}{3043}}}} = 1 + \frac{1}{11 + \frac{1}{1 + \frac{1}{2 + \frac{2463}{3043}}}}$$

$$= 1 + \frac{1}{11 + \frac{1}{1 + \frac{1}{2 + \frac{1}{\frac{3043}{2463}}}}} = 1 + \frac{1}{11 + \frac{1}{1 + \frac{1}{2 + \frac{1}{1 + \frac{580}{2463}}}}}$$

$$= 1 + \frac{1}{11 + \frac{1}{1 + \frac{1}{2 + \frac{1}{1 + \frac{1}{\frac{2463}{580}}}}}} = 1 + \frac{1}{11 + \frac{1}{1 + \frac{1}{2 + \frac{1}{1 + \frac{1}{4 + \frac{143}{580}}}}}}$$

Here we truncate the development of the continued fraction; calculations (see below) show that with the approximation here obtained, the whole number ratio is accurate to within 0.028 days. We convert back to a simple fraction:

$$1 + \frac{1}{11 + \frac{1}{1 + \frac{1}{2 + \frac{1}{1 + \frac{1}{4}}}}} = 1 + \frac{1}{11 + \frac{1}{1 + \frac{1}{2 + \frac{1}{\frac{5}{4}}}}} = 1 + \frac{1}{11 + \frac{1}{1 + \frac{1}{2 + \frac{4}{5}}}}$$

$$= 1 + \frac{1}{11 + \frac{1}{1 + \frac{1}{\frac{14}{5}}}} = 1 + \frac{1}{11 + \frac{1}{1 + \frac{5}{14}}}$$

$$= 1 + \frac{1}{11 + \frac{1}{\frac{19}{14}}} = 1 + \frac{1}{11 + \frac{14}{19}}$$

$$= 1 + \frac{1}{\frac{223}{19}} = 1 + \frac{19}{223} = \frac{242}{223}$$

The ratio of the draconitic month to the synodical month is therefore approximately equal to $242 : 223$.

Indeed

$$242 \cdot 27.2122 \text{ days} = 6585.352 \text{ days}$$

and

$$223 \cdot 29.5306 \text{ days} = 6585.324 \text{ days}$$

The average of these two values is 6585.338 days.

With 365.25 days in a year, this amounts to somewhat more than 18 years. If we take into account the actual leap years that fall into this time period, then the 18 years represent $365 \cdot 18 + 4 = 6574$ days (or, if 5 leap years fall into this time period, then 6575 days).

The remainder is 11.338 days; but 0.338 days constitute $0.338 \cdot 24 = 8.112$ hours ≈ 8h and 7m. The total time is thus 18 years, 10 or 11 days, 8 hours and 7 minutes (more exact calculations give about 10 minutes rather than 7). This is the so-called Saros-cycle, in which a solar eclipse is approximately repeated in the same way. The 8 hours represent about a third of an additional day; this means that the earth has rotated about $\frac{1}{3}$ of a revolution and so the eclipse only is visible in a similar geographic location only after three Saros-cycles have passed.

V. Conclusion

At many points, the study of the higher calculations allows for exciting connections with real-world applications; among these we include the example just presented above. It can appear as the crowning jewel to mark the end of the lesson block provided one has had the time beforehand to practice the processes involved in developing continued fractions with several further examples. Other applications (of exponentiation) can be found, for example, in population growth or in the study of radioactivity.

Logarithms and the Logarithmic Spiral

Peter Baum

Exponentiation is handled in the 10th grade.[6] This can be followed by the treatment of logarithms. Historically, logarithms did not arise as the inverses of exponentiation, but rather through a comparison of a geometric sequence of numbers with an arithmetic sequence of numbers. Archimedes had already recognized as much[7]. In a short work titled "The Sand Reckoner," he formulates the following: "If a geometric sequence is given whose terms are denoted by $a_1, a_2, a_3, \ldots$ and whose initial term $a_1 = 1$, then $a_m \cdot a_n = a_{m+n-1}$."

The pastor Michael Stifel (1487? – 1567) was a pioneer in the field who employed exponential notation for the numbers in a geometric sequence, was the first to use the word 'exponent,' and extended the rows to negative exponents:

9	8	7	6	5	4	3	2	1	0	-1	-2	-3	-4
512	256	128	64	32	16	8	4	2	1	$\frac{1}{2}$	$\frac{1}{4}$	$\frac{1}{8}$	$\frac{1}{16}$

The reduction of multiplication and division within a geometric sequence to addition and substraction in the arithmetic sequence of the exponents was known among the "cossists," but was not generally felt to be of any great use because the gaps in the geometric sequences were too large. However, there were two possible ways by which such a sequence could be made more dense:

1. to shrink the base, as seen when comparing the powers of two with the powers of three

2. to allow fractional exponents.

The first possibility was chosen by the ingenious Jost Bürgi[8], a clockmaker and mathematician on the court of Baron Wilhelm IV in Kassel, at the first observatory in Europe. With Bürgi's help, Wilhelm was able to improve the angular precision of his instruments from 1-2 minutes to about 20 seconds. He recommended Tycho Brahe, a Dane who was younger by 13 years, to the king, Friedrich II. He kept in close contact with Brahe, and the best astronomical data of the time was achieved in Kassel and on the island Hven. Wilhelm knew that Bürgi played a critical role in this fact, and referred to him as a 'second Archimedes'. Because Bürgi was unable to read Latin, he commissioned Nicolaus Reimarus, who was also in Kassel at the time, for a translation of the major works of Copernicus into the German language– the first of its kind. In 1603, at the request of Kaiser Rudolf, Bürgi travelled to Prag, where he befriended Johannes Kepler, the assistant of Tycho Brahe. Kepler thought very highly of him.

Bürgi began around 1588 – after his time in Kassel – to reduce the gaps in the geometric sequence through a brilliant idea: he chose the base 1.0001. Because the decimal notation with the period was not common at the time, Bürgi used a small circle, but he often omitted it. A table was formed that had 8 columns and 51 rows on each printed page; this table was, however, not printed until

---

[6]Cf. the article "The Higher Calculations" by Markus HÜNIG in this book.

[7]ARCHIMEDES: The Sand Reckoner. In: Works. Translated by A.Czwalina. Wissenschaftliche Buchgesellschaft Darmstadt 1963, p.357

[8]E.VOELLMY: Jost Bürgi und die Logarithmen, Beiheft Nr.5 in the journal „Elemente der Mathematik", Basel 1948

1620. Kepler was familiar with the table and probably used it already in his enormous calculation of the orbit of Mars, and he was upset that Bürgi waited so long with its publication.

In Bürgi's table, with the title "Arithmetic and Geometric Progression Tables," the logarithms (exponents) are listed along the edge in the first column and in the first row, and the black numbers in the middle are eight-digit powers of the base 1.0001.

The calculation was relatively simple, because to obtain the successor of any number in the geometric sequence, one ten-thousandth part of it must be added to it. This is how the density of the table is obtained: neighboring numbers differ from one another only in their ten-thousandth part. With the aid of spreadsheet software (e.g., OpenOffice or Excel), such a table is easy to construct for the purposes of demonstration. We include here two samples from pages 1 and 58 of the 'progression tables':

Page 1

	0	50	100	150	200	250	300	350
0	1,00000000	1,00501227	1,01004966	1,01511230	1,02020032	1,02531384	1,03045299	1,03561790
1	1,0001	1,00511277	1,01015067	1,01521381	1,02030234	1,02541637	1,03055603	1,03572146
2	1,00020001	1,00521328	1,01025168	1,01531534	1,02040437	1,02551891	1,03065909	1,03582503
3	1,00030003	1,00531380	1,01035271	1,01541687	1,02050641	1,02562146	1,03076216	1,03592861
4	1,00040006	1,00541433	1,01045374	1,01551841	1,02060846	1,02572403	1,03086523	1,03603221
5	1,0005001	1,00551488	1,01055479	1,01561996	1,02071052	1,02582660	1,03096832	1,03613581
6	1,00060015	1,00561543	1,01065584	1,01572152	1,02081259	1,02592918	1,03107141	1,03623942
7	1,00070021	1,00571599	1,01075691	1,01582310	1,02091467	1,02603177	1,03117452	1,03634305
8	1,00080028	1,00581656	1,01085798	1,01592468	1,02101677	1,02613438	1,03127764	1,03644668
9	1,00090036	1,00591714	1,01095907	1,01602627	1,02111887	1,02623699	1,03138077	1,03655033
10	1,00100045	1,00601773	1,01106017	1,01612787	1,02122098	1,02633961	1,03148391	1,03665398
11	1,00110055	1,00611834	1,01116127	1,01622949	1,02132310	1,02644225	1,03158705	1,03675765
...	...		...		...		...	

Page 58

	22800	22850	22900	22950	23000	23050	23100	23150
...	...		...		...		...	
22	9,79709485	9,84620053	9,89555234	9,94515152	9,99499930	10,04509693	10,09544566	10,14604676
23	9,79807456	9,84718515	9,89654190	9,94614603	9,99599880	10,04610144	10,09645521	10,14706136
24	9,79905436	9,84816987	9,89753155	9,94714065	9,99699840	10,04710605	10,09746485	10,14807607
25	9,80003427	9,84915468	9,89852130	9,94813536	9,99799810	10,04811076	10,09847460	10,14909088
26	9,80101427	9,85013960	9,89951116	9,94913017	9,99899790	10,04911557	10,09948445	10,15010579
27	9,80199437	9,85112461	9,90050111	9,95012509	**9,99999780**	10,05012048	10,10049440	10,15112080
28	9,80297457	9,85210973	9,90149116	9,95112010	**10,00099780**	10,05112549	10,10150445	10,15213591
29	9,80395487	9,85309494	9,90248131	9,95211521	10,00199790	10,05213061	10,10251460	10,15315112
30	9,80493527	9,85408025	9,90347155	9,95311042	10,00299810	10,05313582	10,10352485	10,15416644
31	9,80591576	9,85506565	9,90446190	9,95410573	10,00399840	10,05414113	10,10453520	10,15518185
...	...		...		...		...	

Actually, in Bürgi's table, the comma is missing by the black numbers and a zero is included by all of the red numbers, probably to facilitate interpolation[9]. The resulting base problem of this "logarithm table" may be read about in more depth in the Voellmy reference. Bürgi referred to the exponent that yields the power 10.00000000 as the whole red number and calculated it through interpolation to 23,027.0022. Indeed

$$1.0001^{23027.0022} = 9.9999999967 \quad \text{and} \quad 1.0001^{23027.0023} = 10.0000000967$$

[9]In the original, the numbers in the top row and the leftmost column of each page of the table are red.

From $1.0001^x = 10$ it follows that $x \cdot \log 1.0001 = \log 10 = 1$

The calculation $1 : \log 1.0001$ leads to the more precise value $x = 23,027.0022033$. The whole red number is needed for multiplication or division by 10.

The second possibility for reducing the gaps in the geometric sequence was chosen by the Scotsman John Napier (1550 − 1617), also known as Lord Neper. At first, he also had a geometric sequence constructed using a number close to 1, namely 0.9999999. The publication of his "Descriptio mirifici logarithmorum canonis" in 1614 caused the Englishman Henry Briggs (1556 − 1630) to suggest the number 0.1 as the base of a logarithm table. Both of them later decided to use the base 10, which was adopted by Briggs after Neper's death and lead to his 1617 publication of "Logarithmorum Chilias prima," in which he calculated the logarithms to 8 decimal places.

There were subsequently many mathematicians[10] who calculated further tables, including, among others, Johannes Kepler.

Although the calculator has made the use of logarithms somewhat obsolete, the act of looking up numbers in large tables is still quite relevant, and this can be effectively demonstrated for the students here. The calculation of a logarithm should also be demonstrated (here we calculate log 2). The calculation is performed by squaring the number repeatedly until it is larger than 10, and then dividing by 10 and repeating. Through this process it is possible to obtain approximations that are ever closer to the true value.

$10^x = 2$ $\qquad\qquad 0 < x < 1$

$10^{4x} = 16$

$10^{4x-1} = 1.6$ $\qquad\qquad 0 < 4x - 1 < 1 \qquad\qquad 0.25 < x < 0,5$

$10^{32x-8} = 42.94967296$

$10^{32x-9} = 4.294967296$ $\qquad\quad 0 < 32x - 9 < 1 \qquad\quad 0.28125 < x < 0,3125$

$10^{64x-18} = 18.446744...$

$10^{64x-19} = 1.8446744...$ $\qquad\quad 0 < 64x - 19 < 1 \qquad\quad 0.296875 < x < 0,3125$

$10^{256x-76} = 11.5792089...$

$10^{256x-77} = 1.15792089...$ $\qquad 0 < 256x - 77 < 1 \qquad 0.3008 < x < 0,3047$

$10^{4096x-1232} = 10.4438888...$

$10^{4096x-1233} = 1.04438888...$ $\quad 0 < 4096x - 1233 < 1 \quad 0.301025 < x < 0,30127$

$\qquad\qquad\qquad\qquad\qquad\qquad\qquad\qquad\qquad\qquad\qquad \log 2 = 0.30102999566...$

---

[10]MORITZ CANTOR: Vorlesungen über die Geschichte der Mathematik, Bd.2 S.718 ff. Leipzig 1913

R. WOLF: Handbuch der Astronomie Bd.1 S.68 ff. Zürich 1890, Reprint 1985

R. GEBHARDT (Hrsg.):Rechenbücher und mathematische Texte der frühen Neuzeit (Schriften des Adam-Ries-Bundes Annaberg-Buchholz; 1999 Bd. 11

J. HAMEL: Die astronomischen Forschungen in Kassel unter Wilhelm IV., Frankfurt 1998

L. v. MACKENSEN: Die erste Sternwarte Europas ... , München 1979

Once the logarithms of two prime numbers a and b have been calculated, the logarithms of the product and quotient of a and b can easily be obtained from the following rules:

$$\log(a^n \cdot b^m) = n \cdot \log a + \log b$$

$$\log\left(\frac{a^n}{b^m}\right) = n \cdot \log a - m \log b$$

The different growth processes – the arithmetic sequence in the logarithms and the geometric sequence in the powers – can be made clear if the regular growth of the exponents in the horizontal direction is compared with the increasing growth of the powers in the vertical direction. In this way we create the exponential curves $y = a^x$ where $a = 2$, $a = 3$, $a = 1.5$ in the Cartesian coordinate system.

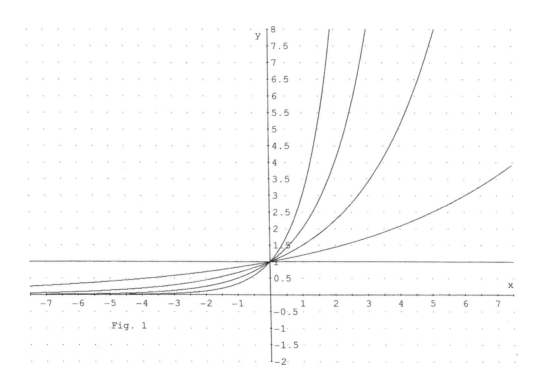

Fig. 1

Notice: all of the curves cut the y-axis in the point $B(0,1)$, and the x-axis is an asymptote. The larger the base a is, the steeper the curve is to the right of the y-axis and the quicker it approaches the asymptote. For the base $a = 1$ the degenerate case occurs – a line through B parallel to the x-axis. If the reciprocal a^{-1} of a number a is chosen as the base, the resulting exponential curve is the mirror image across the y-axis of the exponential curve for a.

The hand-drawn tangents to the curves at the point $B(0,1)$ differ from one another through the angle α which they form with the x-axis. To each of these angles α there corresponds a particular base a. Which base corresponds to the angle $\alpha = 45°$? We call that number e; it lies between 2 and 3. Later, one can refer back to this point and derive, from the difference quotient, the formula

$$e = \lim_{n \to \infty} \left(1 + \frac{1}{n} \right)^n.$$

Ernst Bindel[11] hit upon the brilliant idea of constructing a representation of an exponential sequence in polar coordinates as follows: first the x-axis is wrapped around a circle of radius 1 that has center $M(0, -1)$. The ordinates of the exponential curve which represent the integer powers are usually drawn vertically above the x-axis, so when this is wrapped around the circle, they extend from the circle radially outward like the quills of a porcupine. The resulting points lie on a spiral that spins farther from the circle as it is traversed clockwise and spins asymptotically closer to the circle as it is traversed counter-clockwise.

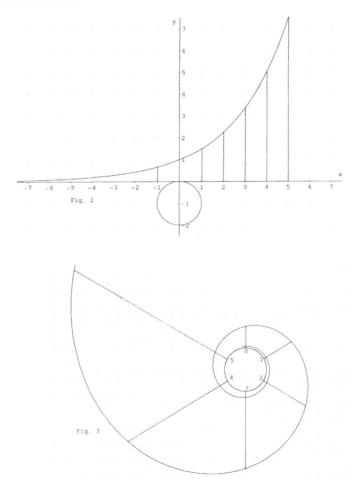

Fig. 2

Fig. 3

The exponents 0, 1, 2, 3, 4, 5 and 6 lie on the circle, and indeed, almost exactly in a regular hexagon. This is because the circumference of the unit circle is $2\pi \approx 6.28$, which is nearly 6. So

---

[11] ERNST BINDEL: Logarithmen für Jedermann, 3rd edition, Stuttgart 1983

it is not terribly far off, for this drawing, to place these exponents on the regular hexagon and to mark off the corresponding powers radially outward[12]. As the final step, we truncate each of the spiral radii by 1 unit and thus we obtain the Bernoulli, or logarithmic, spiral[13]:

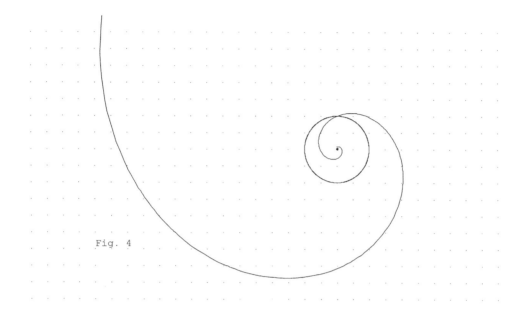

Fig. 4

The curve spirals counter-clockwise inward, but without ever reaching the pole of the spiral, the middle point $M(0, -1)$. For this reason, the point is often called the asymptotic point, or eye, of the spiral. In the figure, the base $a = 1.5 = 3 : 2$ was chosen.

If we now consider the exponents 0, 1, 2, 3, 4, 5, 6, ... and their respective points on the spiral: A, B, C, D, E, F, G, ... with respective radii: $1, 3/2, 9/4, 27/8, 81/16, 243/32, 729/64, \ldots$ then we may note that, when joined to the middle point, they form similar triangles: MAB ~ MBC ~ MCD ~ MDE etc.. This is because the angle at M is always $60°$ and neighboring radii always have the proportion $a = 3 : 2$.

Bindel now enumerates five characteristic properties of the logarithmic spiral that Bernoulli found:

1. The spiral is a loxodrome; that is, all of the spiral radii form a constant angle α with the corresponding spiral tangent.

2. If we form the mirror image of the spiral through any tangent line and let the one spiral roll along the other, the then pole describes a congruent spiral. Bernoulli named these cycloids.

3. If every point of a curve has a unique circle of curvature, then the geometric locus of all the centers of curvature is called the evolute of the curve. The original curve is then referred to

---

[12] In this way, one actually still obtains a perfectly legitimate logarithmic spiral, but just with the base $b = a^{\frac{3}{\pi}}$.
[13] JAOKOB BERNOULLI (1654 −1705)

as the involute. Every curve is thus the involute of its evolute. The logarithmic spiral has the property that both its evolute and its involute are congruent to the original logarithmic spiral.

4. If each center of curvature is reflected across the corresponding tangent line to the spiral, then a congruent spiral is again obtained, the anti-evolute.

5. If the pole of a spiral is thought of as a light source whose light is reflected on the spiral, then the reflected light forms the envelope of yet another congruent spiral, the caustic.

The interested reader can read Bindel for more about these properties. A drawing from Bernoulli can also be found there, from which a simple construction of the center of curvature can be read off using a right triangle; however, Bindel does not mention this fact. It can be made plausible if one is willing to delve a bit into the question of the arclength and the properties of the evolute:

Although the spiral winds infinitely often around the asymptotic point, its pole or 'eye', the curve has a finite arclength between the pole and any point on the spiral. This can be shown – assuming the properties of evolutes – in the following manner.

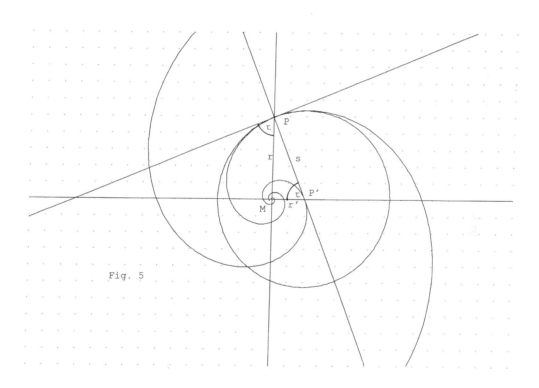

Fig. 5

At an arbitrary point P on the spiral – we have chosen a point here on the y-axis for simplicity – let the tangent and the corresponding normal lines be drawn[14]. The center of curvature P′ lies on the normal line [15]. Therefore its tangent P′P also forms the same angle τ with the corresponding

---

[14]The tangent forms a constant angle τ with the corresponding radial line *MP* (see property 1 above).

[15]It describes a congruent spiral with the same pole *M*, the evolute (see property 3 above).

radial line MP′. Because the normal is perpendicular to the tangent,

$$\angle MPP' = 90° - \tau \text{ and thus } \angle P'MP = 90°.$$

So, on the one hand, $s = P'P$ represents the radius of curvature of the original spiral, and on the other hand, it is the length of the entire evolute between the point P and the asymptotic point M. So if we wrap this segment around the evolute like a taut string, the point P traverses the original spiral, the involute of the evolute, until it coincides with the pole M. In order to understand this, a solid grasp of evolutes and involutes of many other simple curves is required. Certainty comes about through the interplay between geometric visualization and precise definitions. This experience can serve as an introduction to (an initial conception of) the infinitely small[16]. Because $r = MP$ and $r' = MP'$ are the radii, we apparently obtain the following simple relationship:

$$s \cdot \cos \tau = r' \quad s \cdot \sin \tau = r \quad r' \cdot \tan \tau = r$$

From Figure 5, a remarkable property intimately associated with the evolute can be observed; noting that, to each point P′of the evolute there corresponds a similar right triangle P′MP : If a logarithmic spiral is rolled along its tangent line, then the pole travels in a straight line.

It is not possible to prove, with 10th graders, the equation $\ln a \cdot \tan \tau = 1$. One deduces this fact from an infinitesimal consideration that can be posed in the 12th grade:

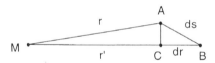

Let M be the pole, and A, B be two points on the spiral that are close to one another. Then the angle $dx = \angle AMB$ is very small. Let C denote the base point of the altitude dropped from A to MB, let $MA = r$ denote the radius of point A, let $MB = r'$ denote the radius of point B, and let $\tau = \angle ABC$ be the angle between the tangent line and the radius. The smaller dx is, the more closely $MC \approx -MA = r$ and $r' = r + dr$. With $AC = r \cdot dx$ we obtain

$$\tan \tau = \frac{r \cdot dx}{dr} \quad \text{or} \quad \frac{dr}{dx} = \frac{r}{\tan \tau}.$$

From $r = a^x = e^{x \ln a}$ it follows that $\frac{dr}{dx} = \ln a \cdot e^{x \ln a} = \ln a \cdot r$

and thus

$$\tan \tau = \frac{1}{\ln a}.$$

A few years ago, a very nice book was published by Klett-Verlag[17]. In this book, many different spirals are presented, along with their interesting properties and historical connections. It also

---

[16]The arclength and radius of curvature associated with a point P on the spiral can be calculated if one knows the constant angle τ and the radius of P.

[17]JOHANNA HEITZER: Spiralen. Ein Kapitel phänomenaler Mathematik. Leipzig 1998

contains a rich bibliography for further reference. The standard reference for curves of all sorts was compiled by Loria[18]. Before the Bernoulli brothers, the logarithmic spiral was studied by René Descartes (1596 − 1650) and Evangelista Toricelli (1608 − 1647). Descartes defined it to be a curve in which the ratio of the arclength to the radius is constant.

Many spirals appear in nature. One of the most beautiful can be found by cutting open, along the plane of symmetry, the shell of the Nautilus Pompilius, a cephalopod of the Pacific ocean. How can we determine whether or not this is a logarithmic spiral?

Recall from the beginning that similar triangles arise from the spiral points belonging to integer exponents. This can be easily checked for the nautilus spiral. An equi-angular bundle of 6 lines (mutually adjacent lines meeting at an angle of 30°) is placed on the copy of the nautilus spiral so that the center of the bundle lies on the pole. Then the points of intersection of the bundle with the spiral are marked and many triangles are obtained, whose similarity can be checked. If P_n and P_{n+1} are two neighboring spiral points, then both the angles $\alpha_n = \angle MP_nP_{n+1}$ must be equal and the ratios of neighboring radii must agree.

The angle 30° corresponds to a circular arc of length $\frac{\pi}{6}$. For the ratio of neighboring radii, then we obtain

$$\frac{r_n}{r_{n+1}} = r = a^{\frac{\pi}{6}}.$$

From this we can calculate the base of the spiral:

$$a = r^{\frac{6}{\pi}}$$

The pole, however, can be somewhat difficult to recognize on the copy of a nautilus spiral. It can be determined as follows: for an arbitrary direction, one draws all the parallel tangents with their points of tangency to the spiral. These points must lie on a line that passes through the pole (a polar line). The tangent lines that are perpendicular to these give rise to points that determine a second polar line, one that is perpendicular to the first. These two polar lines intersect each other at the pole.

The base of the spiral can also be determined through the use of the tangent lines. If we denote by t_n, $n = 1, 2, 3, ...$ the sequence of tangent lines from the outside inward, then the tangents t_n and t_{n+2} parallel. Their distances apart a_n form a geometric sequence of numbers, whose quotient must be $q = a^{\frac{\pi}{2}}$. From this we can compute the base: $a = q^{\frac{2}{\pi}}$. From the drawing one also obtains the tangent angle (the angle between the tangents and the corresponding radial line).

The following table lists the measurements of an actual nautilus spiral according to the method described.

---

[18]GINO LORIA: Spezielle algebraische und transzendente ebene Kurven, Theorie und Geschichte. German edition by Fritz Schütte, Leipzig 1902

n	r_n in mm	angle in °	$r_{n-1}:r_n$	base
1	83	64.5		
2	75	65.0	1.107	1.214
3	67.5	64.0	1.111	1.223
4	60.5	63.0	1.116	1.233
5	54	66.5	1.120	1.242
6	50	66.0	1.080	1.158
7	46	66.0	1.087	1.173
8	42	64	1.095	1.19
9	38	65.0	1.105	1.211
10	35.0	65.0	1.086	1.17
11	31.5	64.0	1.111	1.223
12	28.5	64.0	1.105	1.211
13	26	66.5	1.096	1.192
14	24	66.0	1.083	1.165
15	21	66.0	1.083	1.165
16	19.5	65	1.143	1.29
median		**65**	1.102	**1.204**
standard deviation		1.023	0.02	0.035
relative error		1.6%	1.5%	2.9%

distance between parallel tangents

n	a_n	$a_{n-1}:a_n$	base
1	126		
2	93	1.355	1.213
3	70.5	1.319	1.193
4	53	1.33	1.199
5	40.0	1.325	1.196
median		1.332	**1.200**
standard deviation		0.014	0.008
relative error		1.0%	0.6%

tangent angle:	78.5
tan:	4.915
ln(base)	0.203
base:	**1.226**

The extremely small deviance from the ideal is indeed amazing. With the appropriate software (eg, Derive), one can print out a spiral with the calculated base onto a transparency and lay this over the nautilus spiral. It is impressive for the students to see how precisely the exact logarithmic spiral fits the spiral of the nautilus. The exponential growth of the nautilus is understandable: the amount of the growth depends on the size of the animal at that moment.

The following two diagrams illustrate the method described.

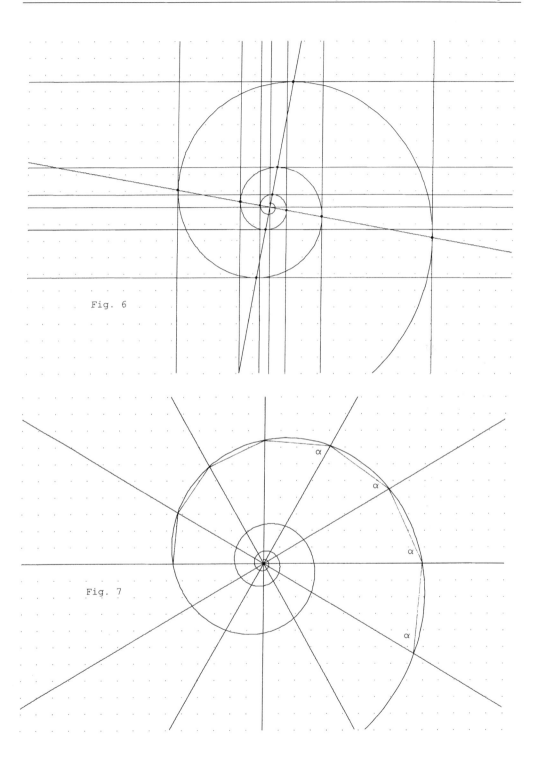

Fig. 6

Fig. 7

On Numerical Relationships in Music

Karl-F. Georg

Preliminary Remarks

Although the use of logarithms as a basis for simplifying hand calculations has become obsolete, their treatment in the 10th grade should by no means be omitted. Simple examples of such calculations can be demonstrated to make their historic usage clear. Because logarithmic functions and their applications cannot be discussed until the students have reached analysis, there is an opportunity in the 10th grade to consider the existence of logarithmic patterns in the context of musical intervals. The students are familiar with the necessary musical background, while arithmetic and geometric sequences, as well as exponential and logarithmic calculations, have just been covered.

Therefore it is possible to investigate the subjects of music and mathematics, and how they work together in the perception and experiencing of tones. The first time I worked through this material was in a class that did not have access to music lessons. Later experience, however, proved that it is very desirable for students to be able to see the relationship of mathematics with another subject, and the unit serves well not only to review the basics of music, but to delve deeper into them.

As a concluding application, the Weber-Fechner Law can be discovered and formulated. This result forms a bridge between the physical and psychological realms,.

For the most part I have based this work on the presentation of *Ernst Bindel,* (1985) "Die Zahlengrundlagen der Musik im Wandel der Zeiten" and "Logarithmen für Jedermann" (1983), as well as *Hermann von Baravalle,* "Physik als reine Phänomenologie" (Baravalle). More information about the Weber-Fechner Law can be found in *Bengt Ulin,* "Der Lösung auf der Spur." Additional references that may be helpful are *Peter Michael Hamel,* "Durch Musik zum Selbst" and *Eberhard Schröder,* "Mathematik im Reich der Töne."

Some intentional repetition appears in the chapters so that the students can more easily transition to the new contexts.

I. Consideration of the Monochord

The monochord was introduced to students in 6th grade physics, where they were shown the relationship between string length and musical intervals. The central tenet of the Pythagorean school (ca. 540 BC) that "number is all" was made palpable. Now this theme is to be taken up once again.

Let a string be tuned to the note C (the base note). If a bridge is held at the midpoint of the string then when the divided string is plucked, the octave c^1 is sounded. Similarly, if two strings are plucked, whose lengths have a ratio of 1 : 2 (part : whole), then the octave will be heard. If a bridge is held at $\frac{2}{3}$ of the (base note) string length, then the fifth sounds, and the fourth results at $\frac{3}{4}$ of the string length.

128

1 ————————	base note	(eg. c)
$\dfrac{1}{2}$ ————	octave	(c^1)
$\dfrac{1}{4}$ ——	2nd octave	(c^2)
$\dfrac{2}{3}$ ————	fifth	(g)
$\dfrac{1}{3}$ ——	octave of fifth	(g^1)
$\dfrac{3}{4}$ ————	fourth	(f)
$\dfrac{3}{8}$ ——	octave of fourth	(f^1)

In a range of two octaves, the string lengths of the notes $c : c^1 : c^2$ have ratios of $4 : 2 : 1$. For the intervals depicted in Fig. 1, the ratios of the string lengths (relative to the base note c) have the following proportions (the third row is obtained from the second through multiplication by 24):

$$
\begin{array}{ccccccccccccc}
c & : & f & : & g & : & c^1 & : & f^1 & : & g^1 & : & c^2 \\
1 & : & \tfrac{3}{4} & : & \tfrac{2}{3} & : & \tfrac{1}{2} & : & \tfrac{3}{8} & : & \tfrac{1}{3} & : & \tfrac{1}{4} \\
24 & : & 18 & : & 16 & : & 12 & : & 9 & : & 8 & : & 6
\end{array}
$$

Each note corresponds to a certain frequency. The shorter a string is, the faster it vibrates. The frequency and the string length are inversely proportional and we obtain the following ratios of the frequencies:

$$c : c^1 : c^2 = 1 : 2 : 4$$

and further

$$
\begin{array}{ccccccccccccc}
c & : & f & : & g & : & c^1 & : & f^1 & : & g^1 & : & c^2 \\
1 & : & \tfrac{4}{3} & : & \tfrac{3}{2} & : & 2 & : & \tfrac{8}{3} & : & 3 & : & 4 \\
6 & : & 8 & : & 9 & : & 12 & : & 16 & : & 18 & : & 24
\end{array}
$$

(the third row is obtained from the second through multiplication by 6).

These intervals within an octave form the scale of the greek lyre: c, f, g, c^1.

We experience the sequence of steps $c \rightarrow c^1$, $c^1 \rightarrow c^2$, $c^2 \rightarrow c^3$, each of which is an octave, as *equal* steps, even though the frequency ratios are *not* equal steps, but rather $1 : 2 : 4 : 8$. If we write this sequence in exponential notation

$$1 : 2 : 4 : 8 = 2^0 : 2^1 : 2^2 : 2^3$$

then the equal steps appear in the exponents!

II. The Natural Harmonic Sequence and Overtones

In order to investigate this regularity we have found, we divide the monochord string (base note *C*) into ever decreasing segments that correspond to the following fractions: $\frac{1}{2}$; $\frac{1}{3}$; $\frac{1}{4}$; $\frac{1}{5}$; $\frac{1}{6}$; ... A sequence of notes is formed: the octave (*c*); the octave of the fifth (*g*), because a third of the whole string amounts to $\frac{2}{3}$ of the half; then at $\frac{1}{4}$, the octave of the octave (*c¹*); then the major third over the 2nd octave (*e¹*); at $\frac{1}{6}$ the minor third after that (*g¹*); and at $\frac{1}{7}$ the string sounds an even smaller interval, a 'too small' minor third; etc.

This sequence of tones is called the *natural harmonic sequence*. The discovery of this interval division of a string and the accompanying acoustical experience was offered as proof in the ancient world of the connection between nature and the soul: the intervals are physical phenomena and the numeric ratios correspond to specific feelings. It was only in the 17th century that *Marin Mersenne* (1588 – 1648, french philosopher, mathematician and music theorist) discovered that in a vibrating string, tuned to a base note like *C*, there also sound a number of further, very quiet accompanying notes, which are called *overtones*. A tone forms, together with its overtones, a sound. The frequencies of these overtones stand in whole number ratios to that of the base note; they form, with the base note, the natural harmonic sequence. (The regular structure was described in 1702 by *J. Sauveur*). The overtones can be heard on a monochord or any string instrument by lightly touching the string at the above described places (Flageolet tones).

The natural harmonic sequence has been physically detected as far as the 40th overtone. A particular mixture of overtones affords each instrument its own characteristic *timbre*.

Overtone sequence (Flageolet tones) of the c-string of a cello:

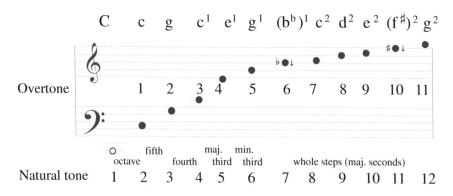

Fig. 2

III. The Development of the Major Scale from the Natural Harmonic Sequence [19]

From the figure above it is apparent that the successive natural numbers of the natural harmonic sequence reflect the relative frequencies of the corresponding tones. From this, we can see that,

---

[19]This derivation of the major scale differs from the pythagorean tuning principle, which is built from the fifth and does not use the frequency ratio $\frac{5}{4}$ of the major third. This further step was taken by Didymos (born 63 BC). This tuning method is called diatonic.

in the time that the base note C completes one vibration, its second octave c^1 completes four, its major third e^1 completes five, and the fifth g^1 completes 6 vibrations. In this way, the major chord $c^1\ e^1\ g^1$ has frequency ratios $4:5:6$. These ratios hold for every major chord, regardless of what the base note is!

The major chords   have frequency ratios

the tonic c: $c - e - g$ $4:5:6$

the upper fifth g: $g - b - d^1$ $4:5:6$

the lower fifth F: $F - A - c$ $4:5:6$

We consider these three major chords in relation to each other:

$$4 \ : \ 5 \ : \ 6$$
$$c \ - \ e \ - \ g$$
$$F \ - \ A \ - \ c \qquad g \ - \ b \ - \ d^1$$
$$4 \ : \ 5 \ : \ 6 \qquad 4 \ : \ 5 \ : \ 6$$

Scaling proportionately so that equal numbers appear at the junctions of the major chords, we obtain:

$$24 \ : \ 30 \ : \ 36$$
$$c \ - \ e \ - \ g$$
$$F \ - \ A \ - \ c \qquad g \ - \ b \ - \ d^1$$
$$16 \ : \ 20 \ : \ 24 \qquad 36 \ : \ 45 \ : \ 54$$

If we bring all of these notes into the octave $c - c^1$, we obtain (ascending an octave by doubling, descending an octave by halving the frequencies):

$$f \ - \ a \ - \ c \ - \ e \ - \ g \ - \ b \ - \ d$$
$$32 \ : \ 40 \ : \ 24 \ : \ 30 \ : \ 36 \ : \ 45 \ : \ 27$$

Rearranging these notes according to increasing frequency leads to the C-major scale:

$$c \ - \ d \ - \ e \ - \ f \ - \ g \ - \ a \ - \ b \ - \ c^1$$
$$24 \ : \ 27 \ : \ 30 \ : \ 32 \ : \ 36 \ : \ 40 \ : \ 45 \ : \ 48$$

If we assign the relative frequency of 1 to the base note c in this scale, then we obtain the following numeric interval sequence:

unison		second		maj. third		fourth		fifth		maj. sixth		maj. seventh		octave
c	–	d	–	e	–	f	–	g	–	a	–	b	–	c^2
1	:	$\dfrac{27}{24}$	:	$\dfrac{30}{24}$	:	$\dfrac{32}{24}$	:	$\dfrac{36}{24}$	:	$\dfrac{40}{24}$	:	$\dfrac{45}{24}$	:	$\dfrac{48}{24}$
1	:	$\dfrac{9}{8}$	:	$\dfrac{5}{4}$	:	$\dfrac{4}{3}$	:	$\dfrac{3}{2}$	:	$\dfrac{5}{3}$	:	$\dfrac{15}{8}$	:	2
1	:	1.125	:	1.250	:	1.333	:	1.500	:	1.666	:	1.875	:	2

We choose to use exponential notation for the last row (with base 2):

$$2^0 : 2^{0.170} : 2^{0.322} : 2^{0.415} : 2^{0.585} : 2^{0.737} : 2^{0.907} : 2^1$$

The exponents are the base-2 logarithms of the ratios in this row. Multiplying these exponents (logarithms) by a thousand, we obtain the sequence:

unison	second	major third	fourth	fifth	major sixth	major seventh	octave
0	170	322	415	585	737	907	1000

	*170	152	93	170	152	170	93

* Difference sequence of individual steps

There are only three (!) different step sizes in the major scale:

$$170 \equiv \text{major tone}$$
$$152 \equiv \text{minor tone}$$
$$93 \equiv \text{half step}$$

This can also be made clear graphically using a logarithmic scale (Fig. 3):

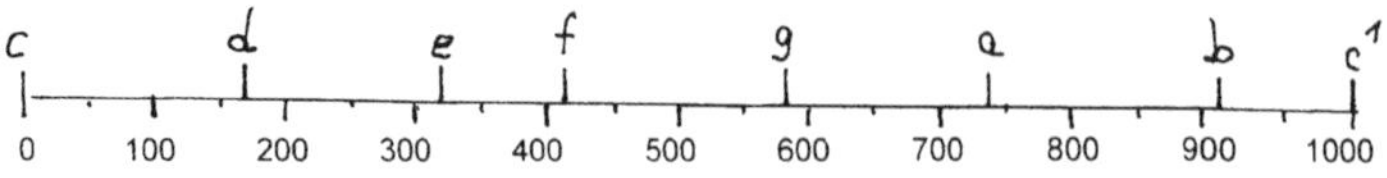

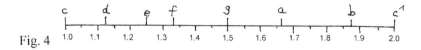

Fig. 3 0   100   200   300   400   500   600   700   800   900   1000

Contrast this with a linear scale, which from the sequence (cf. above) 1 : 1.125 : 1.250 : ... yields:

Fig. 4   1.0   1.1   1.2   1.3   1.4   1.5   1.6   1.7   1.8   1.9   2.0

IV. Major Scales, Minor Scales – Intervals

The two fundamental scales in today's music are the major and minor scales:

major scale		minor scale	
interval	interval numbers (frequency ratios)	interval	interval numbers (frequency ratios)
unison	1	unison	1
second	$\dfrac{9}{8}$	second	$\dfrac{9}{8}$
major third	$\dfrac{5}{4}$	minor third	$\dfrac{6}{5}$
fourth	$\dfrac{4}{3}$	fourth	$\dfrac{4}{3}$
fifth	$\dfrac{3}{2}$	fifth	$\dfrac{3}{2}$
major sixth	$\dfrac{5}{3}$	minor sixth	$\dfrac{8}{3}$
major seventh	$\dfrac{15}{8}$	minor seventh	$\dfrac{9}{5}$
octave	2	octave	2

The ratios of the individual steps (= intervals) between any two successive notes can be calculated as follows. e.g.:

$$\text{fourth} - \text{fifth} \quad \frac{3}{2} : \frac{4}{3} = \frac{9}{8} \left(= \frac{405}{360} \right) \text{ major tone}$$

$$\text{major third} - \text{fourth} \quad \frac{4}{3} : \frac{5}{4} = \frac{16}{15} \left(= \frac{384}{360} \right) \text{ semitone}$$

$$\text{minor third} - \text{fourth} \quad \frac{4}{3} : \frac{6}{5} = \frac{10}{9} \left(= \frac{400}{360} \right) \text{ minor tone}$$

With both of these scales, we note the ratios of the steps:

major scale

	1		$\frac{8}{9}$		$\frac{5}{4}$		$\frac{4}{3}$		$\frac{3}{2}$		$\frac{5}{3}$		$\frac{15}{8}$		2

steps

$\frac{9}{8}$	$\frac{10}{9}$	$\frac{16}{15}$	$\frac{9}{8}$	$\frac{10}{9}$	$\frac{9}{8}$	$\frac{16}{15}$

minor scale

	1		$\frac{9}{8}$		$\frac{6}{5}$		$\frac{4}{3}$		$\frac{3}{2}$		$\frac{8}{5}$		$\frac{9}{5}$		2

steps

$\frac{9}{8}$	$\frac{16}{15}$	$\frac{10}{9}$	$\frac{9}{8}$	$\frac{16}{15}$	$\frac{9}{8}$	$\frac{10}{9}$

We can see that both scales are formed from three different intervals:

$$\frac{9}{8} \equiv \text{large whole step}; \quad \frac{10}{9} \equiv \text{small whole step}; \quad \frac{16}{15} \equiv \text{half step}$$

When the major and minor scales are presented in a logarithmic scale, then the various positions of the the whole tones, semitones, and intervals can be compared.

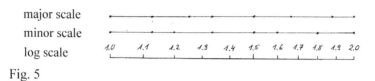

major scale

minor scale

log scale

Fig. 5

V. Just Intonation

On each note of the C-major scale, a new major scale can be built, for example, a "D-major" or an "E-major", etc., each of which has the same ratios in the logarithmic scale. If we draw these scales below one another (see Fig. 6), then it becomes apparent that, in many places, the points (= "positions" of the notes) of the different scales do not line up exactly, and thus have different frequency ratios in relation to the base note C. So, for example, the "same" note *e* has different positions, as the third in *C*-major or as the second in *D*-major.

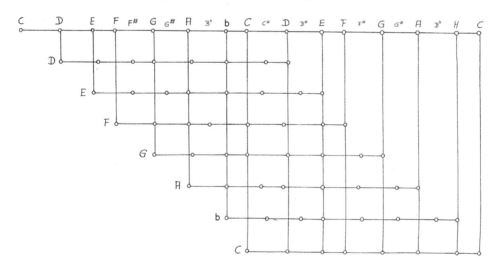

Fig. 6: Graphical representation of the major keys in just intonation (log scale)

Calculation confirms this: note *e*

1. as major third of C-major: $1 \cdot \frac{5}{4} = \frac{5}{4} = \frac{80}{64}$

2. as major second of D-major: $\frac{9}{8} \cdot \frac{9}{8} = \frac{81}{64}$

134

The value of the second fraction is thus $\frac{1}{64}$ (= 1.56%) larger. The note e (as second) in *D*-major is thus higher than in *C*-major.

Remark: In order to calculate the relative frequency of a note that is given as an interval over a base note, we simply multiply the frequency of the base note by the interval ratio. For example, to calculate f sharp as the major third over d: relative frequency of $d = \frac{9}{8}$, major third: $\frac{4}{5}$, therefore f sharp has the relative frequency $\frac{9}{8} \cdot \frac{5}{4} = \frac{45}{32} \approx 1.406$.

VI. Well-tempered Intonation

All of the intricacies of the different keys – the different positions of the "same" note – might be fine for a violinist, because he creates his notes anew each time he plays them. But they create nearly insurmountable problems for anyone building an instrument with fixed notes (e.g., a spinett, organ, flute), because the instrument cannot simultaneously sound "in tune" in different keys. One attempt to solve this problem was the Thompson organ (in 19th century) with 53 notes per octave, although it was barely playable.

In 1691 the organist *Andreas Werckmeister* published a text "Musical Temperament" in which he offered "a clear and true mathematical exposition of how , through instruction with a monochord, a piano, or particularly the various kinds of organs – the positive organ, the regal, the spinet, or other such – can be well-tempered so that, in today's manner, all keys and modulations can be enjoyed in a pleasant and bearable harmony." In this work, he put forward his suggestion to divide the octave into twelve equal half-steps. Of course this would imply that none of the intervals would be exactly perfect, but the discrepancy is not large enough to be bothersome. But now, for example, c sharp can be turned into d flat, d sharp into e flat, etc.; one can play music in all keys and modulate from one to the other. With that, *J.S. Bach* had the necessary means to compose *The Well-Tempered Clavier*, in which he wrote preludes and fugues through all of the different key signatures.

So what is the mathematical basis for equal-tempering? The "space" between unison and octave is divided into 12 equal half-steps, or semitones. So there is no longer any distinction between a large whole step and a small whole step! On a logarithmic scale, then, all of the semitones lie at equal distances apart. So the exponents (logarithms) of the relative frequencies must proceed in equal steps. Thus we have the following sequence of frequencies for the well-tempered major scale (cf. corresponding example in Ch. III.): [20]

unison	second	major third	fourth	fifth	major sixth	major seventh	octave
2^0	$2^{\frac{2}{12}}$	$2^{\frac{4}{12}}$	$2^{\frac{5}{12}}$	$2^{\frac{7}{12}}$	$2^{\frac{9}{12}}$	$2^{\frac{11}{12}}$	2^2
2^0	$2^{0.167}$	$2^{0.333}$	$2^{0.417}$	$2^{0.583}$	$2^{0.750}$	$2^{0.917}$	2^1
1	1.1225	1.2599	1.3348	1.4983	1.682	1.8877	2

---

[20]For a semitone, the ratio of the frequencies of two neighboring tones is $q = 2^{\frac{1}{12}} = \sqrt[12]{2}$, because after 12 half-steps, an octave must $q^{12} = 2$ be reached ($q = 1.05946$).

If we multiply the exponents by a thousand, we obtain the sequence of steps

unison	second	major third	fourth	fifth	major sixth	major seventh	octave
0	166.67	333.33	416.7	583.33	750	916.67	1000
	*166.67	83.33	166.67	166.67	166.67	166.67	83.33

* sequence of distances between steps

We see that we have achieved our goal!

Comparison of just and equal-tempered intonation through juxtaposition of the base-2 logarithms (multiplied by a thousand):

	just	equal temper
unison	0	0
second	170	167
maj. third	322	333
fourth	415	417
fifth	585	583
maj. sixth	737	750
maj. seventh	907	917
octave	1000	1000

The maj. third, sixth, and seventh suffer the largest displacement.

Through temperament (from latin for balancing, equalizing) it is now possible to construct the circle of fifths. Beginning from C in the upper circle in Fig. 7, if we move right (up the scale) by a fifth (7 half steps), then we land on G. This step is indicated by the line joining $C - G$.

Now we move another fifth to D, etc. We obtain in this way the sharp key signatures. If we begin again at C and move left by fifths (F, B flat, E flat, ...), we obtain the flat key signatures. If we take twelve fifths in one direction ($C \to G \to D \to ...$), then we land back at the 'starting note' C. For the minor keys the same is true. Here it makes sense, though, to start with A.

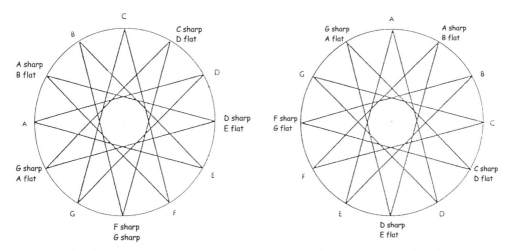

Fig. 7a: Circle of fifths for the major keys   Fig. 7b: Circle of fifths for the minor keys

If one were to ascend from C by 12 *perfect* fifths, however, then one would land at an end tone that is higher than the C in the 7th octave. This is shown in the following table of relative frequencies:

sequence of fifths			sequence of octaves		
fifths	note	rel. freq.	rel. freq.	note	octaves
	c	1	1	c	
first					
	g	$\frac{3}{2} = 1.500$			first
second			2	c^1	
	d^1	$\left(\frac{3}{2}\right)^2 = 2.250$			second
third			4	c^2	
	a^1	$\left(\frac{3}{2}\right)^3 = 3.375$			
forth					third
	e^2	$\left(\frac{3}{2}\right)^4 = 5.063$			
fifth					
	b^2	$\left(\frac{3}{2}\right)^5 = 7.594$	8	c^3	
sixth					forth
	$(f^\sharp)^3$	$\left(\frac{3}{2}\right)^6 = 11.391$			
seventh			16	c^4	
	$(c^\sharp)^4$	$\left(\frac{3}{2}\right)^7 = 17.086$			
eighth					fifth
	$(g^\sharp)^4$	$\left(\frac{3}{2}\right)^8 = 25.629$			
ninth			32	c^5	
	$(d^\sharp)^5$	$\left(\frac{3}{2}\right)^9 = 38.443$			
tenth					sixth
	$(a^\sharp)^5$	$\left(\frac{3}{2}\right)^{10} = 57.665$			
eleventh			64	c^6	
	$(e^\sharp)^6$	$\left(\frac{3}{2}\right)^{11} = 86.498$			seventh
twelfth					
	$(b^\sharp)^6$	$\left(\frac{3}{2}\right)^{12} = 129.746$	128	c^7	

This difference of relative frequencies of $\Delta = 1.746$ appears to the listener as approximately a quartertone, or an interval of $129.746 : 128 = 1.0136$. This discrepancy is called the "pythagorean comma".

VII. Tonal Range Numbers

With an interval, e.g., an octave, we associate a musical, emotional experience. We experience different octaves as tonal steps (tonal ranges) of the same kind (cf. Ch. I). The two notes C (64 Hz) and c^1 (256 Hz) cover a tonal range of two octaves. In the discussion that follows, we will use the notion of intervals (= spacings) along with the notion of tonal ranges.

In the following display, we see the relationship between interval numbers (in relative frequencies) and tonal ranges (here octave ranges):

$$
\begin{array}{cccccl}
1 & 2 & 4 & 8 & 16 & \text{interval} \\
c^1 & c^2 & c^3 & c^4 & c^5 & \\
0 & 1 & 2 & 3 & 4 & \text{octave range}
\end{array}
$$

Now we consider some intervals and their tonal ranges, whereby we recall that with the latter, we found the following relationship when we introduced logarithms:

$$
\begin{array}{llllllll}
\text{sequence of powers} & 1 & 2 & 4 & 8 & 16 & 32 \\
\text{can be written} & & 2^0 & 2^1 & 2^2 & 2^3 & 2^4 & 2^5
\end{array}
$$

The exponents, which form an arithmetic sequence, are the base 2 logarithms of the numbers 1, 2, 4, 8, ... The tonal range numbers, therefore, are from a mathematical point of view, logarithms, while the interval numbers represent the corresponding numbers. Thus the tonal range number of an octave is

$$ 1 = \log_2 2 =: \text{Oct.} $$

What then would be the tonal range number of a fifth? The sequence of interval numbers of fifths:

$$
\begin{array}{ccccc}
1 & \frac{3}{2} & \frac{9}{4} & \frac{27}{8} & \dots
\end{array}
\quad \text{reads, in}
$$
exponential notation
$$
\left(\tfrac{3}{2}\right)^0 \quad \left(\tfrac{3}{2}\right)^1 \quad \left(\tfrac{3}{2}\right)^2 \quad \left(\tfrac{3}{2}\right)^3 \quad \dots \quad (*)
$$

In order to compare the fifth with the octave, we again choose the base 2 for the sequence (*) of powers and, by applying the third law of logarithms $\log a^n = n \cdot \log a$, we obtain:

$$
2^0 \quad 2^{\log_2 \frac{3}{2}} \quad 2^{\log_2\left(\frac{3}{2}\right)^2} \quad 2^{\log_2\left(\frac{3}{2}\right)^3} \quad \dots
$$
or
$$
2^0 \quad 2^{\log_2 \frac{3}{2}} \quad 2^{2 \cdot \log_2 \frac{3}{2}} \quad 2^{3 \cdot \log_2 \frac{3}{2}} \quad \dots
$$

Thus, the tonal range of the fifth is characterized by the step $\log_2 \frac{3}{2}$, and its tonal range number is

$$ \text{Fi} := \log_2 \frac{3}{2}. $$

Accordingly we find the tonal range number of the fourth to be:

$$\text{Fo} := \log_2 \frac{4}{3}.$$

The table below summarizes the results for a number of intervals:

	interval number	tonal range number
octave	2	$\log_2 2 =: \text{Oct}$
fifth	$\frac{3}{2}$	$\log_2 \frac{3}{2} =: \text{Fi}$
fourth	$\frac{4}{3}$	$\log_2 \frac{4}{3} =: \text{Fo}$
maj. third	$\frac{5}{4}$	$\log_2 \frac{5}{4} =: \text{Th}$
min. third	$\frac{6}{5}$	$\log_2 \frac{6}{5} =: \text{th}$
ninth	$\frac{9}{4}$	$\log_2 \frac{9}{4} =: \text{Ni}$

With this foundation we can investigate the different tone sequences:

1. We consider the tone sequence $c - g - c^1$. From the base note c a fifth is taken to g, and from here, a fourth to c^1, that is also simultaneously the octave from c. For the interval numbers, we have the following calculation:

$$\text{fifth interval} \cdot \text{fourth interval} = \text{octave interval}$$

$$\frac{3}{2} \cdot \frac{4}{3} = 2$$

For the calculation of the tonal range numbers, which our perception follows ("to the fifth range, a fourth range is combined, or added"), we have:

fifth tonal range	+	fourth tonal range	=	octave range
Fi	+	Fo	=	Oct
$\log_2 \frac{3}{2}$	+	$\log_2 \frac{4}{3}$	=	$\log_2 2$

Now, the number 2 is the same as $\frac{3}{2} \cdot \frac{4}{3}$, and so therefore:

$$\log_2 \frac{3}{2} + \log_2 \frac{4}{3} = \log_2 \left(\frac{3}{2} \cdot \frac{4}{3} \right)$$

and we recognize here the first law of logarithms:

$$\log a + \log b = \log (a \cdot b).$$

2. From c one fifth upwards to g and from g one minor third downwards to e (i.e., the major third from c). Interval number calculation:

$$\text{fifth interval} : \text{minor third interval} = \text{major third interval}$$
$$\frac{3}{2} : \frac{6}{5} = \frac{5}{4}$$

Tonal range calculation:

$$
\begin{array}{ccccc}
\text{Fi} & - & \text{th} & = & \text{Th} \\
\log_2 \frac{3}{2} & - & \log_2 \frac{6}{5} & = & \log_2 \frac{5}{4}
\end{array}
$$

Rule (2nd law of logarithms):

$$\log a - \log b = \log \frac{a}{b}$$

3. $c - g - d$ (fifth to g and then a fifth to d). Interval number calculation:

$$\text{fifth interval} \cdot \text{fifth interval} = \text{ninth interval}$$
$$\left(\frac{3}{2}\right)^2 = \frac{9}{4}$$

Tonal range calculation:

$$
\begin{array}{ccccc}
2 & \cdot & \text{Fi} & = & \text{N} \\
2 & \cdot & \log_2 \frac{3}{2} & = & \log_2 \frac{9}{4} \\
2 & \cdot & \log_2 \frac{3}{2} & = & \log \left(\frac{3}{2}\right)^2
\end{array}
$$

Rule (3rd law of logarithms):

$$n \cdot \log a = \log a^n$$

4. One takes half of the interval $c - d^1$ and arrives at the fifth g from c. Interval number calculation:

$$\sqrt{\text{ninth interval}} = \text{fifth interval}$$
$$\sqrt{\frac{9}{4}} = \frac{3}{2}$$

Tonal range calculation:

$$
\begin{array}{ccccc}
\frac{1}{2} & \cdot & \text{N} & = & \text{Fi} \\
\frac{1}{2} & \cdot & \log_2 \frac{9}{4} & = & \log_2 \frac{3}{2} \\
\frac{1}{2} & \cdot & \log_2 \frac{9}{4} & = & \log \sqrt[2]{\frac{9}{4}}
\end{array}
$$

Rule (4th law of logarithms):

$$\frac{1}{n} \cdot \log a = \log \sqrt[n]{a}$$

In the structure of these tone sequences, we have found the four laws of logarithms. And so our perception of pitches and intervals is not directly tied to the frequency ratios, but rather to their logarithms.

VIII. The Weber-Fechner Law or the Psycho-physical Law

In our observations we have seen that acoustics offer us an interesting interplay between geometric and arithmetic sequences: when a chromatic scale is played (all 12 semitones), one's hearing transmits the impression of an acoustic ladder being climbed whose steps have equal spacing. From the auditory point of view, there is an arithmetic sequence of perceptions. But if one writes down the sequence of frequencies of these notes, then, for equal temperament, one obtains a geometric sequence with the number $q = \sqrt[12]{2}$ as quotient (see VI).

In summary, we can say: when a sequence of similar, perceptible, external, physical sensations forms a geometric sequence, then the human psyche translates the sequence of sensations into an arithmetic sequence. This phenomenon has been named the *Weber-Fechner Law* for its discoverers, *Wilhelm Eduart Weber* (1804 − 1891) and *Gustav Theodor Fechner* (1801 − 1887). This psycho-physical law, that also holds for perception of light, pressure, and temperature, states that: in the process of perception, we perceive the logarithm of the intensity of the sensation, or, said another way: perception follows energy with a logarithmic scale.

IX. A few Remarks About the Workings of the Ear

When soundwaves enter the ear, they hit upon the eardrum which begins to vibrate with the frequencies of the air that works its way to the thin membrane between auditory canal and cavity. The eardrum projects and transports the tone to the inner ear, where it encounters the auditory bones, the smallest bone structure of the human body. These bones are connected to one another with joints and are reminescent of – in a strange miniaturization – the bone structure of the legs and feet. The organs of the inner ear lie in calcaneum, the hardest and least 'alive' of the bones in the entire human body. There we find the cochlea, in whose watery substance a skinlike membrane is suspended. Both the bone and the membrane have the form of a logarithmic spiral (= flat, planar, open curve that infinitely proceeds outward from a central point). This shape is significant because – as we have seen – the relationship between the intervals and the corresponding frequencies (between musical and acoustical structure) correlates precisely with the relationship between the additive structure of the logarithms and the multiplicative nature of the the numbers upon which they are based. The cochlear spirals in our ear are constantly performing logarithmic processes which, when it comes to sounds or music, transform frequencies into intervals.

The tones rush in like a surging billow deep into the cochlea, but then the wave collapses: the energy that was barely detectable before becomes amplified between the eardrum and the so-called oval window by a factor of about ninety (!) – it is freed from its physical substance, the tone is separated from its physical action. The cochlea of the human inner ear is thus the organ in which tones are lifted from the physical body of the human and then are experienced in their purely musical quality in the transcendent realm of the human soul.

Epilogue

We have been able to see how logarithms work in the world of human perception, when the outside world, pressing in on it, sends its effects to the senses. Logarithms are a mediator between the inner and outer worlds. When the human brings, to the outside world, that which he has created in his soul, he has no truer servant than the logarithm. But the logarithm is also a messenger, when this same outer world is reflected in the soul in the form of feelings. From this point of view, we can see the word logarithm itself in a new light, as it is formed by joining the two notions of *Logos* (= word, thought, law) and *arithmos* (= arithmetic, number theory).

"Music is a secret arithmetical exercise of the soul, which is unaware that it is manipulating numbers. Indeed, the soul accomplishes much in the form of subconscious perception, much which it could not perceive consciously. Those people are mistaken who believe that nothing could happen in the soul without it being aware of the fact. After all, it is clear the soul is mathematically active without realizing it, because there is an effect of this subconscious arithmetic – either a pleasure resulting from harmony, or a displeasure from dischord." *Gottfried Wilh. Leibniz* (1646 – 1716), mathematician and philosopher.

"The world sounds. It is a cosmos of spiritually active beings. Thus the dead material is living spirit." *Vassily Kandinsky* (1866 – 1944).

A Generalization of Pascal's Triangle

Uwe Hansen

The numbers

$$\binom{n+1}{k} \text{ for } k = 0, 1, ..., n+1v$$

– a row of Pascal's triangle – represent the construction of an n-dimensional tetrahedron:

```
                1
             1     1
          1     2     1
       1     3     3     1
    1     4     6     4     1
 1     5    10    10     5     1
```

So, for example, a 3-dimensional tetrahedron consists of 4 vertices, 6 edges, and 4 faces. It is, itself, a 3-dimensional solid. In this way, we have the appearance of the numbers $\binom{4}{k}$, for $k = 1, 2, 3, 4$. The connection with the binomial coefficients is enlightening, because, for example, every face is determined by 3 vertices; so with 4 elements – the vertices – one has $\binom{4}{3} = 4$ possibilities of choosing a set of three. Every edge is determined by two vertices; there are $\binom{4}{2} = 6$ possibilities of choosing two elements from a set of 4 elements.

In addition, we have the following incidence relations:

	vertices	edges	faces	solids
vertex	1	3	3	1
edge	2	1	2	1
face	3	3	1	1
solid	4	6	4	1

Here, for example, the first line means: each vertex is incident with one vertex, 3 edges, 3 faces, and one solid.

For the four dimensional tetrahedron we have the following incidence table:

	vertices	edges	faces	hyper planes	4 dimens. solid
vertex	1	$\binom{4}{1}=1$	$\binom{4}{2}=6$	$\binom{4}{3}=4$	$\binom{4}{4}=1$
edge	$\binom{2}{1}=2$	1	$\binom{3}{1}=3$	$\binom{3}{2}=3$	$\binom{3}{3}=1$
face	$\binom{3}{1}=3$	$\binom{3}{2}=3$	1	$\binom{2}{1}=2$	$\binom{2}{2}=1$
hyperplane	$\binom{4}{1}=4$	$\binom{4}{2}=6$	$\binom{4}{3}=4$	1	$\binom{1}{1}=1$
4 dim. solid	$\binom{5}{1}=5$	$\binom{5}{2}=10$	$\binom{5}{3}=10$	$\binom{5}{4}=5$	1

These numbers are a result of the combinatorial consideration: if one vertex, say, is chosen from the five vertices of a four-dimensional tetrahedron, then there are 4 vertices left over; if one chooses one of these, there are $\binom{4}{1}=4$ possibilities, and so the chosen vertex is incident with 4 edges. If one chooses two of the four edges, then there are $\binom{4}{2}=6$ possibilities. So there are 6 faces that pass through the chosen vertex, etc. This is how the numbers of the first row are obtained. The third line means: from the five given vertices, first choose 3, which determine a certain face of the tetrahedron. In this face, there are 3 edges and 3 vertices. Any other vertex, together with the 3 vertices chosen first, determines a hyperplane. Therefore there are 2 hyperplanes that contain the chosen face of the tetrahedron. This face is, of course, also contained in the 1 entire tetrahedron.

The two tables show how the incidence relation can be calculated in the general case. Two copies of Pascal's triangle always appear, whereby the copy below the diagonal is missing a boundary column of all ones.

These considerations can be carried over to a "cube sequence": a 3-dimensional cube has 8 vertices, 12 edges, 6 faces; it counts as one solid. A "2-dimensional" cube is a square with its 4 vertices and 4 edges. A "1-dimensional" cube is a segment with both endpoints. So we have the following arrangement:

$$\begin{array}{cccccc} & & 2 & 1 & & 3 = 3^1 \\ & 4 & 4 & 1 & & 9 = 3^2 \\ 8 & 12 & 6 & 1 & & 27 = 3^3 \end{array}$$

We see that each row-sum is a power of three. Each number, when added to twice the number to its right, gives the number below them in the next row. A four dimensional cube, then, must have 16 vertices, 32 edges, 24 faces, and 8 hyperplanes (3-dimensional). It can be verified that this really is the case, as follows:

Consider 16 vertices with the coordinates (x_1, x_2, x_3, x_4) with $x_i = \pm 1$. Each vertex is thus the intersection point of 4 hyperplanes with the equations $x = x_1, y = x_2, z = x_3, w = x_4$.

From the four hyperplane pairs $x = \pm 1, y = \pm 1, z = \pm 1, w = \pm 1$, we can only ever choose one hyperplane of each pair (hyperplanes in the same pair are parallel), so there must, then, be 2^4 vertices.

The edges of the four dimensional cube are lines of intersection of three hyperplanes. First we choose three of the four hyperplane pairs, for which there are a total of $\binom{4}{3}$ possibilities. Because each hyperplane pair contains two hyperplanes, this number must still be multiplied by 2^3. So there are a total of $\binom{4}{3} \cdot 2^3 = 32$ edges. This line of reasoning leads then to the following numbers: $2^4 = 16$ vertices, $\binom{4}{3} \cdot 2^3 = 32$ edges, $\binom{4}{2} \cdot 2^2 = 24$ faces, $\binom{4}{1} \cdot 2^1 = 8$ hyperplanes. In this way, we obtain the following schema:

$$
\begin{array}{ccccccccccc}
 & & & & & 1 & & & & & \\
 & & & & 2 & & 1 & & & & \\
 & & & 4 & & 4 & & 1 & & & \\
 & & 8 & & 12 & & 6 & & 1 & & \\
 & 16 & & 32 & & 24 & & 8 & & 1 & \\
32 & & 80 & & 80 & & 40 & & 10 & & 1
\end{array}
$$

The binomial coefficients, the numbers in Pascal's triangle, are the coefficients of

$$(a+b)^n$$

The numbers of the "Cube triangle" just derived are the coefficients of

$$(2a+b)^n$$

It holds, namely, that

$$
(2a+b)^n = \sum_{k=0}^{n} \binom{n}{k} \cdot (2a)^k \cdot b^{n-k}
$$
$$
= \sum_{k=0}^{n} \binom{n}{k} \cdot 2^k \cdot a^k \cdot b^{n-k}.
$$

Setting $a = b = 1$, we obtain

$$
3^n = \sum_{k=0}^{n} \binom{n}{k} \cdot 2^k.
$$

So every row sum is a power of three.

A table can be given for the incidence relation, see the next column. Let $n = 5$ be chosen as an example:

Above the diagonal, which consists of all ones, there appear the numbers of the Pascal's triangle. Below the diagonal are the numbers $\binom{n}{k} \cdot 2^k$.

Why the lack of symmetry? We examine the case of the third row of the given schema.

Suppose a certain face is given as the intersection of three 4-dimensional hyperplanes. If we take one or two of these three hyperplanes away, then we obtain the hyperfaces that contain the chosen face. In choosing which to take away, the number of possibilities is given by the binomial coefficients, here $\binom{3}{1}$ or $\binom{3}{2}$ or $\binom{3}{3}$.

When asked about the vertices that lie in the chosen face, however, then I must add, to the three fixed hyperplanes, two more hyperplanes, so that a set of five can intersect. There are four possibilities, since I choose one hyperplane from each pair; thus there are 2^2 vertices in the fixed face. Similarly, one can show that there are $2 \cdot \binom{2}{1}$ edges that lie in this face.

The regular patterns treated here can be summarized in the following generalization:
Suppose we have n containers, each of which contains p balls. All of the balls are different. One ball will be chosen from each of k containers $0 \leqslant k \leqslant n$. How many possibilities are there? There are $\binom{n}{k} \cdot p^k$.

For $p = 1$ we obtain the numbers of Pascal's triangle, which describe the construction of the general tetrahedron.

For $p = 2$ we obtain the numbers that describe the construction of the general cube (or the general octahedron).

	vertices	edges	faces	3-dim faces	hyper-planes	5-dim. solids
vertices	1	5	10	10	5	1
edges	2	1	4	6	4	1
faces	4	4	1	3	3	1
3-dim. faces	8	12	6	1	2	1
hyperplanes	16	32	24	8	1	1
5-dim solids	32	80	80	40	10	1

Surveying in the 10th Grade

Heinz-Christian Ohlendorf

Introduction

Wake-up is around 7 am, equipment is distributed after breakfast, and at 9am the students can be found making their way through the little village to the field, together with their three teachers and assistants, packed with binoculars and theodolites, ranging rods and levelling staffs. Due to the half-hour walk, we stay outside at midday, eat lunch outdoors (or, in bad weather, in a large trailer) and don't head back to the youth hostel until around 4 pm. Between 6-9 pm there is instruction. In the breaks and, on occasion, in the late evening, there are individual students (and naturally also teachers) busy analyzing data: sharing recorded values, angle sums, coordinates, calculating areas, drawings of polygonal curves , site plans, contour lines, and level curves. It is nice in the evenings when Mr. D., the contracting farmer, drops by and gets updated on the latest results. He is genuinely surprised when we tell him that in his 1000 m long field, there is an elevation change of almost 80 m. He is also happy to learn that, by our calculations, the field that he planted with linseed – the field that he had walked off by foot and assessed to be about 4 hectares large – really does come out to 3.96 hectares.

Those were notes from the surveying trip of a 10th grade at the Waldorf school in Kassel. What was special about this trip was that they went to Northern Bohemia in the Czech Republic, and 100 % of the surveying work was contracted. Nearly a third (170 ha) of the cultivated land of an LPG (enormous farming facilities that were formerly state-owned) was to be separated out from the acreage and switched over to biodynamic farming methods. That requires a redivision of the lots into smaller, more workable units, and – to prevent water damage – the repositioning of the furrows so that they lie in the direction of the contour lines of the land. It also means that the substantial boundary and path changes, that were not officially surveyed or recorded but were simply undertaken by the independent authority of the farming community, must be resurveyed. In addition, in accordance with new laws, the land must be officially leased from the original owners, who technically never lost ownership. The original parcels of land, however, were lost in the consolidation of the property and often lie in the middle of what is now a huge field. Therefore, new parcels of equal value must be measured off in other places, if the owners do not just want to lease their lot. For all of these tasks and many others (e.g., construction site preparation), waiting for an official surveying company would be unthinkable in this time of rapid decision-making and with the profound transformations pervading the whole country. So the aid of a school class trained in surveying is eagerly welcomed, and the students are able to enjoy the just pride of being able to provide a much needed service.

It need hardly be mentioned that a much more modest task – producing maps of a few properties and buildings, or of the course of a creek, or of a street, or ascertaining a number of level curves or contour maps – can provide sufficient practical training for the purpose of this 'surveying' block. Great satisfaction can also arise even if the work is not contracted by a client, but is done purely for sport, so to speak: who can draw the nicest and most precise map? Having an actual client, however, increases the seriousness of the project. This is because what must be delivered, in terms of maps and data, must be error-free – a very high standard for such work to meet. The

147

"classroom" environment is exchanged, not simply for a "class trip", but also, to some extent, to become something of a "company" – and that is an experience which is quite suitable for a 16-year old. It is also understood that only colleagues who themselves already have experience in surveying, managing, and most importantly in verifying data, will undertake contracted work on a large scale with their class. This experience can be gained, however, in just a few years, if a math, technology, or geography teacher really gets swept away with enthusiasm for surveying and cartography.

Ever since the founding of the Waldorf school in Stuttgart in the 1920's, surveying has been an important feature of the Waldorf curriculum. It has repeatedly proven to be a lively, real-world, applicable, and inspiring lesson – a lesson in which a real need of the students is met with a cultural subject that is rich with tradition and of special significance. The origin of the "survey trip" can be traced back to a very simple suggestion of *Rudolf Steiner* in lectures on the curriculum for the emerging upper grades at the Waldorf school: "at this age, the youth (must) be instructed in the basic principles of surveying and map drawing. The youth must be able to draw a pasture or a forest on a map ... (and) ... be able to handle levelling instruments" (GA 302).

At the different Waldorf schools, the surveying trip has developed a number of different variations. It is almost always combined with a class trip, so that a new and preferably different terrain can be studied: mountains, plains, coast, etc. Several schools have placed great importance on aesthetics, reducing the mathematical prerequisites, and the use of simple (preferably self-made) instruments (cf. the article by Schupelius in [Ohlendorf 94]). Others have brought their surveying practices closer to contemporary professional methods and have thus acquired for themselves (either used or sometimes even new) theodolites, leveling instruments, etc. Occasionally the surveying has been conducted in connection with the 9th grade farming internship, with a landscape maintenance block, with constructing a path, or with other such activities. There are many other similar variations. The opportunity may present itself to study astronomical observation, when the North Star is needed anyway to determine which direction is north. Studies in geology, botany, geography, or art history can be easily combined with the project if a colleague comes along who can awaken an interest in these topics.

At the school in Kassel, almost all of these variations have arisen at one time or another. In the past few years, a form has been developed in which great value is placed on building up the necessary techniques in stages. Four "maps" are drawn in succession: a hand sketch after the first tour of the property, a map made using a compass and measured in steps, a skeleton map constructed from exact base- and angle-measurement, and finally, a topographical map complete with many specific details. Although one begins with simple observation of the landscape, the level of precision increases at each stage, as do the technical and mathematical means: theodolite and calculator, trigonometry and coordinates are introduced and naturally also diverse drawing implements, e.g., the now somewhat obsolete pantograph. Creating a map, after all, encompasses a definite graphical and artistic aspect; a map is only good when it is also aesthetically pleasing.

If we wanted to formulate a *learning objective* for this surveying project, we could summarize one in just a few words: "to know how a surveyor's map and an elevation chart are created." But after many years of experience, it is clear that this lesson facilitates many further abilities, experiences, viewpoints, and discoveries. These are really the main learning objective. In addition to describing the main points of this "surveying block," we will also attempt to call the reader's attention to such pedagogical opportunities.

I. An Overview of the Surveying Lesson Block

1. Mathematical Preparation

To create a scaled map after surveying without the similarity theorems of geometry is just as unimaginable as reading a given map in order to orient onesself in the landscape. And it is not enough just barely to know the rules of similar figures – that angles remain equal, that segments shrink or expand in equal proportions – but rather, one must have internalized these so much that, at the very least, one can use these basic principles as tools for graphing and calculating. Therefore, beginning about a year before this block, the students must begin learning and practicing how to work with angles and parallels. This is even more the case, naturally, for the more basic aspects of geometry: Pythagoras, areas of triangles, quadrilaterals, etc. (From these mathematical foundations, surveying exercises can be built up that use first the Jacob's staff, then the compass, and finally the plane table. Such exercises could take place as early as the 9th grade).

Of immediate concern in surveying is, of course, trigonometry. The tradition of combining *Trigonometry* with land surveying exercises is time-honored in high school mathematics and shouldn't therefore be considered anything special. What is novel here is the fact that we don't just look to applied problems for motivation, but rather that the trigonometry is developed out of questions of surveying – as a "theory of praxis" – and that the surveying is viewed as primary. In this way, a path is followed that brings mathematical ideas together with experiences in one's own body through the act of surveying in the field. It is to *this end* that we present, through examples, this potential course of study.

We assume the students have been introduced to the basic principles of sine, cosine, and tangent – to their definitions and to the simplest applications in right triangles, possibly even to the law of sines in acute triangles. With this background, the idea of surveying an extended flat surface can be very fittingly and effectively used to motivate a number of topics, including: the extension of the trig functions to angles over $90°$, the teaching of polar and rectangular coordinates, and the familiarization with the so-called unit circle for sin, cos, and tan. These topics can be developed in the classroom as follows (cf. Fig. 1):

We imagine there is an observer at point A who would like to know the position of a sequence of points P_1, P_2, etc., relative to A. For each point, he measures the distance r and the angle φ against an arbitrarily chosen fixed direction, e.g., East. (Professional surveyors actually use a convention that differs from that typically used in mathematics: angles increase in the clockwise direction, and North $= 0°$ in the x-direction). A scaled drawing is to be produced from these measurements.

Possibility 1: The angles φ_1, φ_2 etc. are marked off with a protractor, and the lengths r_1, r_2 ... are measured off to scale with the ruler. (This should be attempted).

Possibility 2: The drawing will be made on fine-grid graph paper. The distances x (abscissa) and y (ordinate) are calculated and the point P is located on the graph paper.

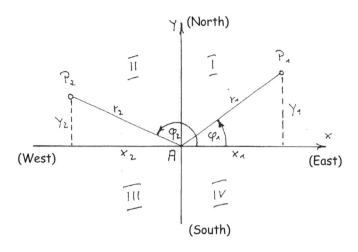

Fig. 1: Coordinate system, Observer at *A*

One quickly notices: Method 1 is more familiar and requires less effort, but Method 2 is more exact! The arguments for 2 win hands-down when we consider that, from a point like P_1, further points will be located, and that the process is to be continued in this manner. This leads to the so-called polygonal curve, one of the most important measuring techniques in practice.

In this way we obtain, directly from the surveying task, a logical introduction to the coordinate systems of an observer at the origin *A*, and the four quadrants are divided by the four compass directions. The sign rules: Quadrant I, *x*- and *y*-values positive; Quadrant II, *x*-value negative, *y*-value positive, etc. are agreements that are close to hand and easy to remember. From this, the concept of sine extends easily to angles $\varphi > 90°$ – e.g., for φ_2 to $\sin\varphi_2 = \frac{y_2}{r_2}$, correspondingly with cosine – all the way up to the drawing of their graphs. The so-called unit circle appears as a useful aid in drawing curves; its appearance from out of thin air as a collection of arbitrary facts to be memorized is just as unnecessary as such a treatment was for the sign rules.

In this way, the conversion from polar coordinates to rectangular coordinates can be introduced and studied in a context that is in no way artificial, but rather is one of the fundamental tasks in the surveying of new points. A variety of exercise problems can be posed, e.g., (Fig. 2) the calculation of the coordinates of P_1, P_2, ... in the above mentioned polygonal curve, in which, at first, the angle is measured in simple cases (compass charting) against the direction north, but then later, also, with the theodolite, the angle is measured against the preceding segment of the polygonal curve. Here arises an fascinating puzzle: how do you find the angle φ_2 formed with the *x*-direction, if you have measured the angle α_2 with respect to AP_1? Even negative angles, like φ_3, can appear. Also the inverse, converting from rectangular to polar coordinates, arises naturally here; the tangent function comes into play, the multiple values of the inverse function, etc.

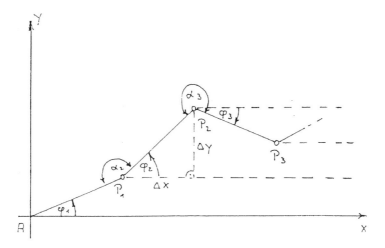

Fig. 2: Polygonal curve from *A*

The *oblique-angled* triangle appears in another typical surveying technique, the "intersection method", generalized to so-called triangulation. In view of the upcoming class trip, the lessons can be structured along these lines: we will be doing this ourselves in a few weeks – and it corresponds (albeit simplified, because we needn't concern ourselves with the curvature of the earth or the height of our measured surface above the assumed map elevation at sea level) to the same procedure that actually has played a major role in the history of field- and geographical- surveying. The typical triangulation diagram can be found on the 10 Mark bill next to *C. F. Gauß*, the pioneer of scientific geodesy. Granted, he was concerned with lofty aims: the theory of statistical errors and the classification of surfaces (curvature) – but the more worldly task concerned was the surveying of the kingdom of Hannover (in 1816).

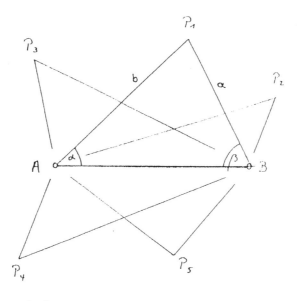

Fig. 3: Intersection method

We imagine a so-called base-segment AB, cf. Fig. 3, that is measured with great accuracy: for us, to within ± 1 cm per 100 m, for the professionals, to within ± 0.5 mm per kilometer! For us, it is between 200 m and 400 m long; one important official base near Göttingen (measured in 1880) is 5.2 km long. A theodolite is placed (hypothetically) on points A, B, that can easily measure the angles α, β to within $\approx 30''$ (seconds), and with the most sensitive setting can measure 100 times more exactly than that. How exactly this works in practice is a topic to be considered later. But if we assume the knowledge of this angle, then the lengths of $a = \overline{BP_1}$ and $b = \overline{AP_1}$ can be calculated using the law of sines – and, in fact, with nearly the same accuracy as the base line, namely, to within centimeters! This exercise should be practiced in all its variations (cf. Fig. 3), particularly with obtuse angles.

The next step to be incorporated with the surveying block, but that still falls within the scope of the usual 10th grade mathematics curriculum, is the calculation of coordinates using the intersection method in simple cases. The coordinate system is layed out as indicated in Fig. 4: the origin at A, the positive x-direction towards B.

We can easily identify two steps in the process:

First step: Calculation of $b_i = \overline{AP_i}$ ($i = 1, 2$... with the law of sines,

Second step: Calculation of the coordinates x_i, y_i of the point in question P_i from the (polar-) data b_i, α_i, where $x_i = b_i \cos \alpha_i$ and $y_i = b_i \sin \alpha_i$.

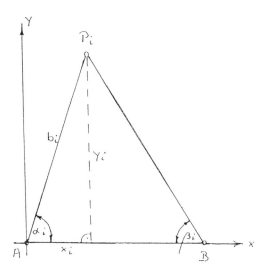

Fig. 4: Simple calculation of coordinates

A number of variations and exercises, which can be covered in the class at this point and which can be geared to the level of the class and of the individual students, will not be discussed here. Our primary aim here is to demonstrate with a number of typical examples how a close connection is possible between the surveying exercise and the mathematical development of trigonometry. A few topics that could be mentioned, however, in this context, are: area computation, height calculation using trigonometry, and, for gifted students, resection and the sum formulas derived from the rotation of coordinate systems.

2. Learning to Use the Instruments in the Schoolyard

A field is to be drawn to scale – a large field that gently slopes upward in waves, that is traversed by two paths crossing each other, and that is bounded by bushes, fences, and a street. Where does one even begin? The idea of laying out *straight* lines and then determining *horizontal* segments doesn't occur to everyone – most students must be told, or even *shown* how to do it! The (urban) meadow just described is located near our school. We divide half of the class into groups of size 4 or 5 and each group is given about 8 ranging-rods. Then lines (alignments) are laid out in a professional manner through simple sighting and manual adjusting.

Who invented the ranging rod? It is an ingenious tool! (The fact that it also serves well for spear-throwing is independently discovered each year by the students.) It must be stood up vertically, which is achieved either by eyeball or with a level, and then the first rod, the one you are standing behind, must block the view of all the others. What is amazing is how a half dozen ranging rods placed precisely in a line at, say, 100 m intervals immediately create a picture of clarity – particularly when the landscape rises and falls a bit – a picture of control, a picture of human intervention into nature. In this day and age, a suspicious person could almost hear the bulldozers rumbling as soon as he sees the red and white line. But at first, there is the satisfying, even proud experience: in the chaos of the natural landscape, something tangible and safe has entered – two fixed points joined by a straight line.

At a very basic level, an attempt can now be made to map the field. The corner points, between which the lines were to be plotted, are not located arbitrarily, but rather at distinguished features of the landscape: path crossings, turns in a path, street edges, fence endings, or along a hedge (Fig. 5).

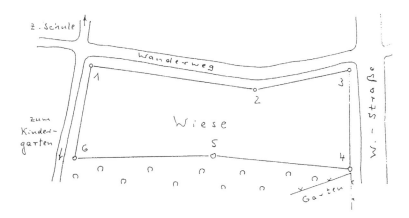

Fig. 5: Site plan of field

Legend:

Garten	-	garden	Wanderweg	-	path
Wiese	-	field	W.-Strasse	-	W. Street
zum Kindergarten	-	to kindergarden	z. Schule	-	to school

So first of all, the *distances* from 1-2, 2-3 etc. need to be measured, specifically, the horizontal distances. There is much to learn about the 5 m-measuring rod: placing, leveling, plumbing, securing, counting, and then reading off the measurement. Measurements made in both directions should agree to within a centimeter. Record-keeping, the manner of writing down the data, and the coordination of all the procedures must be discussed.

Second of all: the *directions* of the lines 1-2, 2-3 etc. must be determined. The compass is used for this purpose. How does one site along the line, and how is the value measured? How can you tell whether or not an iron pipe or something similar has disturbed the magnetic field? And how should this all be notated on a sketch so that the values can be found later? In the next classroom hour, the data will be compared and worked into a small site map, after the other half of the class has already worked out another part (or, for the sake of comparison, the same part) of the field.

In a similar manner, if time allows, three or four other instruments can be tried out on practice areas:

1. Right-angle prism: this serves to locate and place plumb lines in the landscape; with it, one learns to measure individual trees, house corners, etc.
2. Theodolite: the most precise angle measurement device. Four groups are each in charge of one instrument at a corner of the common quadrilateral; the goal is to obtain the correct angle sum.
3. Leveling instrument: the groups compete to measure the height difference between two known locations in the vicinity of the school.

The usual 45-minute class period is not enough for these exercises in the schoolyard. Afternoons from 3 to 5:15 (3 school hours) are often scheduled in the usual afternoon periods. In total, the surveying block is allotted a total of about 4 to 5 weeks in the 10th grade with about 8 hours each week, over and above the usual mathematics lessons. The roughly 14-day excursion occurs within these weeks.

II. Class Trip

1. First walkaround at the new location

We do not need to discuss individually all of the various aspects necessary to organizing a class trip. From the parent-teacher evening concerning the purpose, goals, and costs of the undertaking, to the reservation of buses, from the list of what to pack for each student, to the preview of the rules and the consequences for breaking them – a huge list of preparations. Add to that the crucial decision of location – it's not just anywhere that one finds usable land to survey, and not every youth hostel is ideal for supporting such a surveying group. But the experience is meant to be a high point of the school year – so one puts a bit more effort into it than otherwise. The parents recognize this, too, and help out: cooking parents for unstaffed hostels suddenly volunteer, or a parent with mini-van offers help with transporting equipment and shopping.

Immediately upon arrival, the class walks around the property on a preliminary tour lasting 1-2 hours. Whenever possible, this tour should be conducted under the leadership of a knowledgeable local, particularly when it concerns cultivated land. At this point it begins to dawn on us: we are guests in a different landscape. How do the people here live, how do they interact with their environment ... ? Island or mountain, cottage or field and farm – all these elements combine to form an overall impression. The people speak differently, look different. The point is to get a feel for the lay of the land: how can we orient ourselves, where are north and south, is there a creek, where does the street lead, where to the paths go, etc. Sketching the very first "map" requires taking a first step of abstraction from the simple impressions of the landscape. Therefore, having the students prepare a sketch from memory after walking the land is a good, non-trivial exercise. Perhaps the students can indicate the main direction of a valley, estimate some of the proportions, recall some kinds of foliage, the presence of a field, forest, or meadow, or remember a few steep and flat parts, or draw in some boulders, etc. This first sketch should be colorful, but it should definitely be drawn from a birds-eye view, not a panorama – some students need to be told this! It doesn't matter if the individual maps differ substantially from one another. Naturally there will be students who need more help – in this activity, differences in talent can be very evident.

It is possible, at this point, to begin using the conventional map symbols – evergreen or deciduous forests, lines to distinguish paths, creeks, borders and ditches – this kind of "secret code" is something special, something that the kids really love. One enters into a grown world full of conventions, into a real trade, one with "trade secrets". The drawings, even if they are still certainly quite far off in the proportions, nonetheless begin to look decent. We take our work seriously: the sketches – drawn on paper size A3 (about 12" x 17") – are hung up on the wall, saved, and at the end of the trip, the students smirk as they are compared with the better maps. Based on experience, there are many reasons for such a combination of a walking tour with an observation exercise, and for the task of drawing from recall. We elaborate a bit on two of them.

1. It is not a good idea to ask the students, on the first day, to try to deal with sophisticated instrumentation (or even just with surveying rods and stakes) in the unfamiliar landscape they've just entered. Their first encounter should be more observational, more reserved, and therefore unarmed. Each student's physical body functions, in a natural way, both as a tool and as a measuring apparatus. One can observe not only the eyes, but at least as intensely and as sensitively with the legs! A perceptive walker notices inclines and lengths of paths; the difficult way up the hill becomes longer in the sketch than the flat, horizontal stretches – and with good reason. The measure is still the human being, his walking, his sweating, etc. – the abstraction is just beginning!

2. The imperfection of the walkabout maps motivates anew the use of measuring instruments – without the teacher needing to say a word. This prepares for the work of the following day. Most of the students would be perfectly willing to accept the instruments and to perform the procedures that are shown to them. But the more the students themselves can feel a personal and focused need for sensible tools and rational working procedures, the less overwhelmed they will be by the huge quantity of experiences and traditions, conventions, formalities, and pedantics that have accumulated over the centuries in the field of geodesy and surveying. And with that, the relationship becomes more meaningful between one's own power of reason – which is fully capable of recreating many of the tested methods – and the prevailing methodology that is reflected in the construction of the instruments at hand. In this way, an aspect of genetic learning is attained that plays a particularly important role in surveying and that has long been overlooked.

2. Step Measurement, Compass Mapping

As a first refinement, we transition now to a calibrated step length and the use of a compass (cf. paragraph II.2). A distance of 100 meters is measured off with a measuring tape along a path that is straight and slightly rising, with the beginning and the end marked clearly across the entire width of the path. Each person now walks the path at least six times, three times in each direction. In doing so, they must try to arrive at a regular and reproducible pace, each time making note of the number of steps needed to cover the 100 m. Depending on leg length and temperament, the step lengths will range from 80 cm to over 1 m, and the distribution about the mean is also quite varied: the phlegmatic student arrives at nearly the same number each time with uncanny reliability. The sanguine student tries a different way of walking each time in an attempt to reach an equal pace and perhaps miscounts the steps – the numbers vary accordingly. A few hours later, in the actual surveying, the reliability of this pacing will be put to the test.

The entire lot of land to be surveyed should be divided among groups of four and, to the extent possible, it should be divided so that each group has a closed path around their parcel. This path can then serve as a polygonal curve that can be paced off, and whose turns can be measured with a compass. Ideally, all of the boundary lines are then doubly measured by neighboring groups, providing a useful check on the work (see below). The sketch (Fig. 6) shows, for area III, what is about to be done. In a manner similar to that of section II.2, where the process was described for the school meadow, a row of points is marked off with numbered ranging rods. These should be placed within vision of each other and should approximately follow along the path or boundary lines. The total piece of land could be complicated and encompass several hectares.

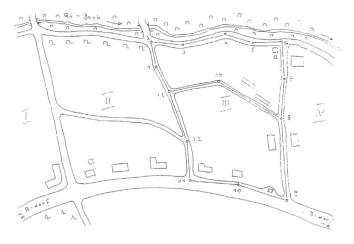

Figure 6: Division for compass survey

Legend:

Qu. Bach	-	creek	A.dorf	-	to town A
B.-dorf	-	to town B			

There are good reasons for trying to let the groups work independently, and, if there are only three adults supervising a class of 30 students, then there really isn't any alternative. For this reason, a system of cross-checking and multiple measurements is implemented, whereby the students themselves can make sure the measurements are made correctly, or at least ensure that gross errors are avoided:

1. A sketch of the polygonal paths is made, something like that in Fig. 6, in which the measured segments can be checked off, so that none of them are forgotten or accidentally swapped.
2. A tabular protocol should be followed, giving the measured values a certain order that helps avoid confusion and mistakes, etc.
3. Additional control measures, like the extra segments passing through the point 14 (Fig. 6), should be built in wherever possible.
4. Paths bounding two regions will be measured by both groups, e.g. the path 11-12-13-1-2 by groups II and III.
5. Each segment will be paced off by 3 students, back and forth in each case. All 6 values will be noted, converted to meters, compared, and the chosen values averaged.
6. The angle of each segment is measured against north with a compass. This measurement is made at both ends, and each time by two students. Attention must be paid to iron pipes, railings, etc., even pocket knives, because they can disturb the compass readings.

The best control measure for a group is the scaled drawing they produce of their entire compass-mapping path. This drawing must form a closed loop, or – if no closed loop was possible in the landscape – then at least connect up with the neighbor's measurements. This drawing, too, should always be created twice and drawn on transparent paper so that, by superimposing them, drawing errors can be quickly spotted.

This entire compass and pacing measurement, from the step calibration to the scaled drawing, takes one day to complete. In the evening, the last of the groups finish their drawings, and it is then – with a few particularly interested students – that the most exciting work begins: putting the pieces together. If everything goes as planned, then, with the help of scissors and tape, a *second* map of the property has been created. In content, this map is much less informative than the first, because no attention has been paid to particular landscape features – but this map is more *accurate*! At first it contains only a scaffolding of polygon constructions, or at the most, a few free-handed additions of some of the most important paths our a few prominent buildings and such. If the property is not too hilly, then the constructed polygons close to within a few meters. A precision of within about $\pm 1\%$ is thus quite attainable. But more importantly, before going to bed, the entire class can be presented with the joint product of their combined day's work. The level of precision attained can be appreciated and respected, but also shortcomings and important omissions of this map are there for all to see. A first impression is formed of the limits of our quick methods – but all that aside, there is a well-earned sense of satisfaction over the (by and large) success of the completed compass map.

3. Construction of a Precise Framework Map – Theodolite and 5 m-Slats

The angle measurement with a compass is exact to within a half of a degree, the foot pacing to within a few meters, so in a drawing scaled at 1 : 1000, errors appear only as millimeters – isn't that exact enough? If we were to replace the foot-pacing by tape measurements, then surely we could create an excellent map – so why bother with tricky optical instruments, careful length measurements, and trigonometric calculation? Not every student asks such questions – for many boys, the complicated technology is the only truth anyway – but the answers must also be sought (here, as in so many other cases) for questions that may remain unspoken, but that nonetheless live below the surface. Even the very pedagogical success of a teacher can often hinge on the ability to sense, to take seriously, and to address appropriately the questions that young people may have about the adult world – questions that are latently present but that remain as yet unformulated. Indeed, the conquering of the world through measuring instruments is, to a large extent, a masculine preoccupation; thus one should all the more try to listen to the reasonable doubt, to that which, more often than not, is likely to arise from the girls. We, ourselves, freely acknowledge that such measurements can only reveal one narrow *aspect* of the world. Particularly in the context of surveying, this point should be appreciated.

Furthermore, the main argument for refinements in technology is not to make the map drawing so much more precise – that will of course also take place – but rather to be able to measure things at all on a larger scale and with that, to gain an overview of much larger areas, without having to pace it all off along the ground step by step. Typically, the theodolite stands on a somewhat elevated location, from which a good view into the distance is possible – only then is it worth having 20-30x telescopic magnification and the amazingly precise technology: angles measured to 1 thousandth of a degree, which corresponds to a lateral error of only 1.6 cm in measurements at distances of 1 km!

For us – following the example of real surveying – the theodolite serves the purpose of creating a net of a few large triangles over the entire area. These triangles are thoroughly verified and they offer, with their vertices, a large-scale structure within which all the specific details can be filled in later. The mathematical ideas underlying the triangle calculation can be seen in Figs. 3 and 4 of the first section. (If some of the important locations cannot be directly measured because they are hidden in a forest or behind a hill, then they can be connected through the use of a polygonal curve, also measured using the theodolite).

Aside from the horizontal angles, there is in principle only *one* segment in the entire structure, the so-called *base*, that must be measured with comparable precision. In this measurement, too, as with the theodolite, we are following the technique (in a simplified manner) that was developed to perfection in the 19th century for the purposes of surveying. This technique for measuring distances amounts to using *slat measurement* with a number of wooden slats that are 5 m long, subdivided into decimeters, and have special steel fittings on the ends that enable them to be positioned to within millimeters.

Understandably, the two kinds of measurement differ substantially in nature. Measuring angles with a theodolite represents the ultimate reliance upon the technology of an instrument. It can easily be carried out by two people: one works the instrument, the other leads the protocol. After the device has been set up, it is centered exactly over the desired point on the landscape using a plumb line. Then, various adjustment knobs are turned, but only with careful touches so that nothing gets displaced. Next, eyepieces and levelling bubbles are observed, and finally, the values are read off the scale. The distant surveying rod to be focused upon must be found in the telescope, crisply brought into focus, and aligned with the crosshairs. Six-digit numbers must be aligned in the display lens, and dictated to the data recorder without error. This activity feels highly scientific, carrying both a sense of honor and responsibility, and is viewed as the high point of all the measurement work. That is fully justified, even if it might, in some weather, turn out to be the case that their fingers and toes are freezing because their own movement in the landscape has been thoroughly eliminated! Thus it can happen that some will conclude that angle measurement is not much more than a lot of annoying "standing around".

The distance measurement is completely different: right from the outset, it smells of primitivity. Carrying two slats around, lining them up end to end, and making little marks on them – what in the world! That is supposed to be a precise measurement? It requires quite an effort on the part of the teacher. He must work alongside the groups and must watch over the process with a relentless attention to detail before it is even halfway recognized that this slat measurement is worth all the trouble. There is much to be gained and learned from mistakes as well, like when the results obtained from measuring back and forth differ from one another. Errors are primarily introduced at one of two points: in lining up the slats, and in counting. Only in landscapes that are extremely flat can the slats be simply laid out end to end. The majority of the time, a plumbline must used to bridge a height difference between two horizontally held slats – that can lead to errors in the scale of decimeters if not done carefully. The other mistake is unexpected, but occurs more frequently: someone miscounts when they make the markings! Usually there are 5 or 10 meters missing at the end, and then, consistently, they are mysteriously also missing on the backwards measurement...

In the big base line measurements in the 19th century (Abendroth), between 60 and 70 soldiers were employed in the task. We must manage the 5 m-slats with 4 to 5 people, but the problem remains the same even in this smaller scale. And here we can speak to at least one example of the multitude of social aspects that are involved in surveying: will it become a communally agreed upon cooperative work – or will everyone get in each others way? In the military, there is a *single* commanding officer. In our surveying group only interest, good will, and practice can ensure that ideas and moods, sensitive feelings and uncertainty of individuals fade away, and that aggravation and quibbling are overcome, not to mention confusion and carelessness. The distance measuring can remain boring and tedious, but it can also develop into an efficient teamwork, if you can manage to get it so that each person watches over the others and does his job at the right moment. A brisk process can emerge out of a clumsy stumbling if the work finds a rhythm and tempo – without losing precision. It is of immeasurable value for the working attitude of the group if this transition can be achieved, whenever possible without intervention from the teacher!

The evaluation of the distance measuring consists primarily of the comparison of the forward and back measurements and an error estimation for a number of intermediate readings. Then the readings are averaged and compared with the results of another group that also measured that distance. The goal is absolute reliability in meters, and safe accuracy into the centimeters with a base line length of 200 m to 400 m.

By contrast, the evaluation of the angle measurement demands much more computational work: the multiple measurements must be averaged (cf. protocol sheet in Fig. 7), the angles in the triangle must be found by subtraction, and the angle sums of the triangles must be checked – that is the best test of correctness. Small differences (up to 0.05 grad) can be distributed, but otherwise, the triangle must be remeasured. (Each group has its own triangles and can check their own work). Then the side lengths of the triangle are to be computed and drawn to scale. For this, the result of the base line measurement is required, or, for further triangulation, the lengths of the sides of other, already known triangles.

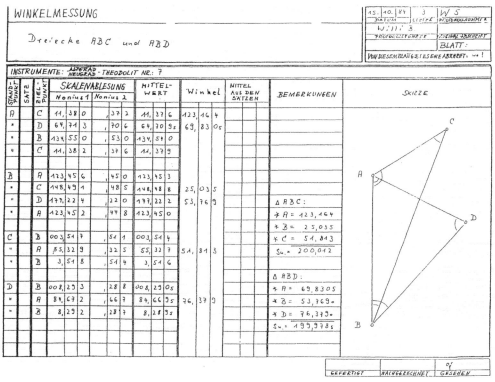

Fig. 7: Protocol of the theodolite measurement

Legend:

Altgrad	-	old scale	Bemerkungen	-	comments
Blatt	-	page	Datum	-	date
Dreiecke ABC und ABD	-	triangles ABC and ABD	gefertigt	-	prepared
gesehen	-	checked	Gruppe	-	group
Mittelwert	-	average	Instrumente	-	instruments
Mittel aus den Sätzen	-	average of records	nachgerechnet	-	recalculated
Neugrad	-	new scale	Nonius 1	-	vernier 1
Nonius 2	-	vernier 2	Original-Abschrift	-	copy
Protokollführer	-	protocol leader	Satz	-	record
Skalenablesung	-	reading	Skizze	-	sketch
Standpunkt	-	position	Su.	-	total
Theodolit Nr.	-	theodolite nbr.	Winkel	-	angle
Winkelmessung	-	angle measurement	Zielpunkt	-	target

Von diesem Blatt gibt es eine Abschrift: wo? - There is a copy of this page: where?

The result of these 2 to 3 days of work should be the completion of a *skeleton map*. To produce this map – first illustrate with 1 or 2 examples – a coordinate computation could be used, as described in Section 1; however, a purely geometric construction with a ruler and a good protractor is also possible. In any case a large portion of the calculation work falls to a group of experts, and the sketching and completion of the first skeleton map is similarly done by volunteer specialists, greatly supported, of course, by the teacher responsible for helping.

With this skeleton map, the height of abstraction has been reached: several days of hard work and nothing more to show for it than one to two dozen points on a big sheet of graph paper! A few might remember, though, that point C represents a crossing of paths, point P was on a pond, etc., but none of this is visible on the paper. The only indication as to what landscape is depicted are a few small polygonal curves that can be seen following along a path and leading to points that were not visible from the base line or other triangulated points.

Additionally, the overview of the whole project is lost for many students through the distribution of the surveying of the triangles among the different groups. This can be countered somewhat in the daily lessons (6 − 7 pm) or in brief orientation discussions before bedtime. The status of the work can be reported, and the tasks of the next day can be announced. (The lesson time can also be used to introduce instruments and new measuring procedures, and to discuss generally the conduct and evaluation of the surveying protocols. Some specific questions only come up during the actual work, when they can be more briefly and sensibly addressed.).

From the above discussion, it is clear that we need to find a way to get back to the details of our portrayal of the landscape, i.e. to that which is most interesting on a good topographical map. The procedures for doing so will be briefly presented in the next two sections.

4. Detail Surveying

In the second week, the skeleton map will be filled in with details. A connection must be made back with the provisional maps that were drawn from the first walkabout. We must refocus our attention, and this time systematically, on the details that form the picture of the landscape: field or forest, brook, marsh and pond, street and dirt road, houses, walls, and fences, but also embankments, hills, rocks and so on. Height measurements will be discussed later, first we will consider *layout maps*. One must be able to see what lies where, and how far it extends. According to whether you are dealing with an entire creek, with its accompanying hedges, or just with a property with several buildings and technical equipment, the method of surveying can be somewhat adjusted, both in the level of detail and the scale of the drawing. The basic idea, though, is always the same: start from what has already been surveyed and what has already been marked in the landscape with stakes or little flags as lattice points, and determine where the interesting objects lie *in relation to* this framework. Only in this way can one be in a position later to sketch all that was measured into the map. In the language of mathematics, this means *coordinates*, i.e., determining numerical values that each give the position of a new, so-called detail-point, in relation to a given line and point. In fact, detail surveying is often referred to as coordination, and it is no surprise that the two main surveying techniques in practice correspond to the usual types of coordinates: right (cartesian) coordinates and polar coordinates.

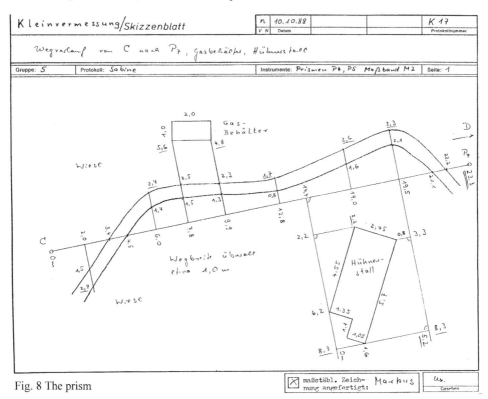

Fig. 8 The prism

Datum	-	date	Gasbehälter	-	gas tank
Gesehen	-	checked	Gruppe	-	group
Hühnerstall	-	chicken crop	Instrumente	-	instruments
Kleinvermessung	-	detail survey	massstäbl. Z. ang.	-	scaled drawing produced
Prismen	-	prisms	Massband	-	measuring tape
Protokoll	-	protocol	Protokollnummer	-	protocol number
Seite	-	page	Skizzenblatt	-	sketch paper
Wegverlauf	-	route	Wiese	-	field

Wegbreite überall etwa 1,0m - path width everywhere about 1.0m

In the first (cartesian) case, one begins from a straight line that is used as a base and then determines plumb lines for position and distance (cf. Fig. 8). The most important tool, aside from the tape measure, is the prism.

(For the sake of brevity, we describe here the somewhat outdated single prism). This consists of an arrangement of mirrors that causes an object which lies laterally perpendicular, like a house corner, to appear as if it lies directly in the line of sight. You now practice – holding the prism in front of your eye – moving back and forth so that your direct vision sees two surveying rods lined up with each other, and through the prism, the house corner appears in the same alignment.

Once this has been accomplished, then you are standing at the vertex of a right angle, thus at the foot of the plumb line of the house corner to the base line. The point is marked on the ground and its position on the base line (x-value) and its distance from the house corner (y-value) are measured. Anyone who has tried for themselves to "find the point," as just described, can understand immediately why this exercise in fine motor skills is very desirable for a young person, and why it is performed with such enthusiasm.

In the second (polar) case, you stand at a point of the skeleton map with an angle measuring device (compass or theodolite) and sight the object from there.

The angle formed with North or another reference direction (φ-value) and the distance (r-value) are measured. In this way, an entire star of lines is determined and drawn to scale afterwards (cf. Fig 9). There are many variations which the students can undertake, depending on the terrain, but we will not digress to describe them all here.

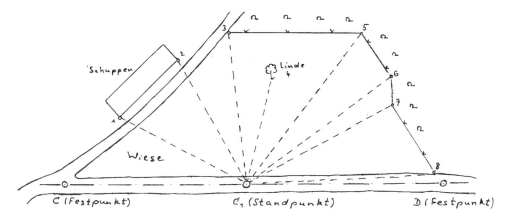

Figure 9: Polar surveying

C (Festpunkt)	-	C (end point)	C1 (Standpunkt)	-	C1 (position)
D (Festpunkt)	-	D (endpoint)	Linde	-	linden
Schuppen		- shed	Wiese	-	field

Hopefully it has become clear through this short description of the activities that there are advantages to this kind of surveying over just sitting in a classroom lecture. In particular, it is much easier to experience for oneself why coordinates and coordinate systems play such a crucial role in modern society. No technology today, from the building of a home to global positioning with satellites, from the simplest construction blueprint to mass production with a CNC machine, takes place without the use of these tools developed from geometry. The aforementioned examples, however, are not primarily concerned with the depiction of something already in existence, but rather with the imposition of human structures into nature; therefore the application of coordinates appears to have an opposite direction to the way it is used in surveying. This, however, is not quite right: the use of rectangular or other coordinates is *always* a human intervention, even in surveying. Only there, it occurs more in its initial stages. But the crucial point is that the landscape is investigated with the particular concepts of the geometer, and so it can respond with nothing other than geometric results. A later reflection upon this quality of human activity is, of course, anticipated precisely through this intensively personal, even physical, act of surveying. None of this, however, is explicitly discussed in the 10th grade.

The biggest challenge for the students is to create the *sketch*, which is supposed to show the approximate position of the surveyed objects, and in which all the measurements are to be recorded (something like Fig. 8, but usually more complicated). The drawing should be clear, the data must be legible to others, the amounts should be unambiguously assignable, each point must be constructible from the indicated values. The measurements must therefore lead directly from known to unknown and accordingly be notated meticulously. Very few students work with the amount of care, and the sense of presentation and context required. The data recorder is responsible for telling the others what still needs to be measured – and he gets the blame if it turns out later than an important measurement was forgotten. Herein lies a small taste of adulthood.

The goal of the detail surveying is for each group to produce a map of its area in a scale of about 1 : 500. It is not a finished product yet, because it contains – in contrast to a usual map – all the measurements from the sketches, so that it can serve as a basis for the actual end product of the surveying trip, the combined map of the surveyed region.

5. Elevation Measurement

So far we have considered, in different variations, maps of *position*, i.e., schematic representations of the landscape from the bird's eye view. And so a question concerning changes in elevation brings with it a new dimension, both in the literal and in the figurative sense. Of course the picture of a landscape remains weak and incomplete without any knowledge of elevation above sea level, slopes, cliffs, valleys, and mountains, and the resulting water movements, climatic influences, etc. For neighborhood settlements and traffic, for agriculture and industry, the vertical aspect of the land is of greatest importance. It is therefore easy to awaken an interest in the subject. Working with a levelling instrument brings new pedagogical challenges, however. The first is to address the thoroughly reasonable question: how do you do that, actually – how do you know, a thousand kilometers from the coast, how high in meters and centimeters a mountaintop is above the average water level of the North Sea near Amsterdam, the so-called Normal Null level (abbreviated N.N.)?

The measurement principle is easy to explain: just create, with the help of an extremely sensitive levelling tube, a very precisely horizontal line of sight and then compare two readings from vertical measuring rods with one another (cf. Fig. 10). The difference between the forward value and the backward value represents the elevation difference between the two locations where the rods are standing.

Such measurements are chained together sequentially. This means that the measuring rods and instrument are alternatingly carried forward, in our sketch, from left to right. (And there is no other way to get from Amsterdam to the Alps...) In putting this astonishingly simple measuring idea into practice, of course, all sorts of surprises can occur – this can be both exciting and beneficial for even the brightest students. Two examples:

1. The level instrument should always stand an equal distance from the two rods – but why? The distance shouldn't actually play any role in questions of height. Could it have something to do with the curvature of the earth? (Not at all, it has much more to do with instrument error).

2. In steeper landscapes it can happen all too easily that, after the most careful placement of the levelling instrument, nothing can be seen in the telescope; the target has disappeared, all that can be seen are blades of grass – or sky and distant woods! Our ability to estimate which line is horizontal in a rising or sloping landscape is simultaneously challenged and trained.

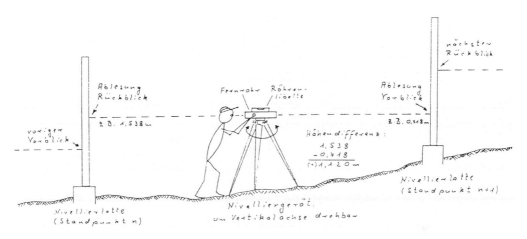

Fig. 10: Elevation measurement with the levelling instrument

Ablesung Vorblick	-	reading (front)	Ablesung Rückblick	-	reading (back)
Fernrohr	-	telescope	Höhendiffernz	-	height difference
nächster Rückblick	-	next back	Nivellierlatte	-	levelling rod
Röhrenlibelle	-	level	Standpunkt n	-	position n
voriger Vorblick	-	previous front	z.B.	-	e.g.

Nivelliergerät um Vertikalachse drehbar - levelling instrument rotatable about vertical axis

Using the method outlined here, only a modest elevation measurement program can be undertaken in a two-week surveying field trip. Groups of 2-3 students each can run through a few 100-meter levelling stretches (as always, in both directions as a check). In this way, elevations can be measured along the important paths or other interesting lines and a few crossings, buildings, mountain peaks, etc., can be entered as data points into the map. A crowning moment of surveying, however, is finding and drawing in a few contour lines for at least a modest part of the landscape studied.

What is interesting about this task is the fact that with contour lines, the *form* of a valley or a hill can be made visible – that brings an impressive element of realism to the map. And far more than in the other detail measurements, the task of creating contour lines requires us again to observe holistically the lay of the land, something which was given up more and more in the production of the skeleton map. Not until the detail surveying did a somewhat more global view of the landscape come back into play, at a higher level of precision than in the first maps that were sketched after the walkabout of the property. It is similar for the elevation measurement: the work with the levelling instruments supplied us with some elevation data that, on their own, add little to the visible quality of the map. But in order to be able to draw contour lines, an intensive study of the surface is needed to produce a large number of points that are determined in both height and position.

A method was selected for our school that is of sufficient accuracy, one which is not only reasonable in its descriptive power, but also time-efficient and requires little technology; it uses a simple hand level [Ohlendorf 94]. Using hand levels, levelling instruments, tape measures, and a pair of surveying rods, a group of three students will plot straight line connections between each pair of previously surveyed heights and will plot many intermediate points that have integer elevations in meters. In this way, elevation scales are formed that cover the landscape as completely as possible.

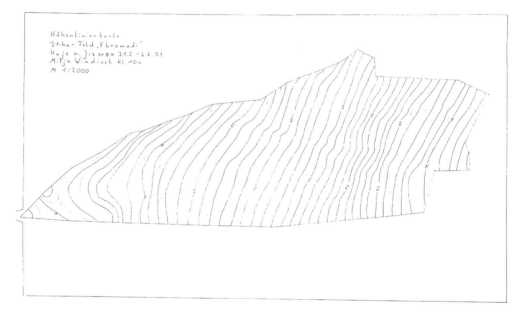

Figure 11: Lines of elevation

Legend

Höhenlinienkarte - elevation map   21-ha Feld - 21-ha field

Points at the same height in the scaled drawing are then connected free-hand. As the final step, it is best to take the finished map and walk the landscape one more time, in order to add a few last details or make some final corrections. With a bit of practice, the work with the hand-level can be completed so quickly that a brisk work rhythm develops – as with the distance measurement with the 5m surveying slats. Gathering the results with an assistant, who checks off the segments one after another in the map and announces the next task, affords a nice overview. This overview awakens an interest in the whole project in such a way that momentum is built which lasts until the network of data is dense enough. For example, in two good days' work, six groups working in parallel measured a total of 1800 points of elevation. With that, an area of 20 ha was covered densely enough with data points that 1 m-contour lines could be drawn (see Fig. 11 above).

III. Conclusion

To create a final product, each student begins from the skeleton map we described earlier, and fills in as many details as possible. Some maps can be drawn in ink on tracing paper so they can be copied for the client, others can be colored in. The students sometimes complete this work when they are back at school. Everyone decides for themselves, with advice from the teacher, whether they want to draw the entire surveyed area, or a piece of it in a larger scale. It is crucial that the map is completed, not that it cover the entire area. As a conclusion to the whole enterprise, the students report on their work at a parent night. The maps and photos of the trip are presented. Parents are fascinated as their children lead them through the use of a compass, theodolite, or hand-level. They tell about the daily routine, describe the land and its inhabitants, and review the whole trip, securing it in their memories before the everyday life of school obscures the special nature of the experience. There are always the inevitable groans about having too little free time, but these are tempered by the pride of having achieved something worthy and meaningful in those two weeks.

The Method of Resection

Peter Baum

In surveying a landscape, it is possible to determine the position of a new point P by measuring the angles α and β between lines of sight to three known reference points L, M, and R. This problem was first solved by Willebrord Snellius in his book "Erathosthenes Batavus" (1617). It has both a practical solution as well as a theoretical solution. The practical solution consists of setting up and orienting a plane table at a new point in the landscape in such a way that this point is indicated on the drawing sheet in the correct location. The theoretical solution consists of calculating the coordinates of the new point from the coordinates of the three reference points and the two measured angles. For this task, the conversion from polar coordinates to rectangular coordinates $(P \rightarrow R)$ and vice-versa $(R \rightarrow P)$ with the help of a calculator is very useful.

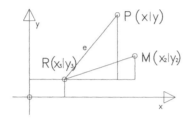

For example, suppose the coordinates of points R and M are known. Then from the two legs $x' = x_2 - x_3$, and $y' = y_2 - y_3$ of the right triangle, the hypotenuse RM can be found in computing $R \rightarrow P$, along with the polar angle φ with $-180° < \varphi < 180°$. If the distance $e = RP$ and the angle $\angle MRP = \delta$ at the new point are known, then the computation $P \rightarrow R$ with $e = RP$ and the polar angle $\varphi + \delta$ leads immediately to the coordinates $x'' = x - x_3$ and $y'' = y - y_3$, along with $x = x'' + x_3$, and $y = y'' + y_3$ where the appropriate sign is chosen. We will refer to this method of calculating coordinates as the "polar attachment" of a new point.

In the ninth edition of the well-known Göschen booklet Nr. 469, "Vermessungskunde II" from *Werkmeister/Großmann*, three solutions are described: the Kaestner solution, which assumes knowledge of goniometric formulas, the Collin solution, and the Cassini solution. The latter two can be treated in the classroom and will be presented here. (Unfortunately, the Collins and Cassini solutions are no longer treated in the newly revised edition by Heribert Kahmemen.)

I. Problem description

From a new point P, three reference points are sighted: L (left point), M (middle point), and R (right point).

First it must be investigated whether, or under what conditions, the position of P can be uniquely determined at all.

The key to this question is the theorem on peripheral angles. According to this theorem, all the points that subtend equal angles in reference to a segment $s = LM$ lie on a circle that passes through L and M. This circle can be constructed by copying the chord-tangent angle α to L or M. Its diameter d can be calculated with the formula

$$d = \frac{s}{\sin \alpha}.$$

In this way, the three circles can be determined that circumscribe the triangles PLM, PMR, PRL and that intersect at P. This point of intersection is only undetermined when the three circles coincide, and are therefore identical with the circumscribed circle about LMR. This happens when P lies on this circumscribed circle.

II. Solution of Willebrord Snellius (1580 – 1626)

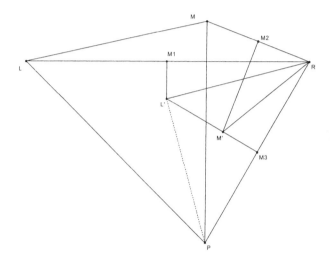

Snellius made use of the following theorem: A central angle in a triangle is twice as large as the corresponding peripheral angle.

Let M_1, M_2, M_3 denote the midpoints of the segments RL, RM, RP and suppose the perpendicular bisector m_3 intersects the perpendicular bisector m_1 at L' and the perpendicular bisector m_2 at M'. Then $\alpha = \angle RPL = \angle RL'M_1$ and $\beta = \angle RPM = \angle RM'M_2$.

Therefore the points L', M', M_3 and finally P can be constructed and calculated in succession as follows:

1.
$$\overline{RL'} = \frac{\overline{RL}}{2 \cdot \sin \alpha}.$$

2. Coordinates of L', through polar attachment of L' on RL with the angle $\angle LRL' = 90° - \alpha$.

3.
$$\overline{RM'} = \frac{\overline{RM}}{2 \cdot \sin \beta}.$$

169

4. Coordinates of M', through polar attachment of M' on RM with the angle $\angle MRM' = 90° - \beta$.

5. Calculation of the angle $\gamma = \angle M'L'R$ through $R \rightarrow P$ with the calculator.

6. Coordinates of P through polar attachment on $L'M'$ with the distance $L'P = L'R$ and the angle $\gamma = \angle M'L'R = \angle M'L'P'$.

III. Solution of John Collins (1625 − 1683)

The Collins solution is based on the circle circumscribed about PLR and proceedes from the following figure:

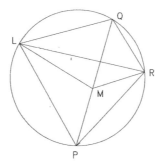

Fig. 1

By copying the angles $\alpha = \angle RPM$ and $\beta = \angle LPM$ to the points L and R, respectively, we find the auxiliary point Q leading to the circle LQR. The line QM intersects this circle at point P. The point P can also be found without the circle by applying the two angles $\delta = \angle LQM$ and $\varepsilon = \angle RQM$ at R and L respectively against the segment LR.

IV. Solution of Giovanni Domenico Cassini (1625 − 1712)

The Cassini solution uses the circles circumscribed about PLM and PRM to construct P. The calculation of the coordinates is achieved by means of polar attachment of the new point P to the segment RM with the help of the calculated values $e = RP$ and $\delta = \angle MRP$.

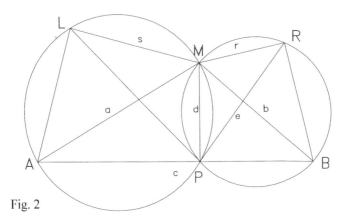

Fig. 2

Suppose $\angle LPM = \alpha$ and $\angle RPM = \beta$ are the angles measured at P. The perpendicular at P to the segment PM intersects the circumscribed circles at A and B. By the theorem of Thales, $a = AM$ and $b = BM$ are diameters of these circles. From this we obtain the simple angle relationships:

$$\angle LMA = 90° - \alpha \quad \text{and} \quad \angle RMB = 90° - \beta$$

The segment $e = RP$ can be obtained by applying the law of sines to the triangle MRP:

$$e = \frac{r \cdot \sin(\beta + \delta)}{\sin \beta}.$$

The segment $AB = c$ can be computed in the triangle ABM with the law of cosines:

$$c^2 = a^2 + b^2 - 2 \cdot a \cdot b \cdot \cos\mu,$$

as well as the angle $\delta' = \angle MBA$ through

$$\delta' = \arccos \frac{b^2 + c^2 - a^2}{2 \cdot b \cdot c}.$$

In order to compute c, we need the angle $\mu = \angle AMB$, which can be found from α, β and $\gamma = \angle LMR$ by using:

$$\mu = \gamma - (90° - \alpha) - (90° - \beta) = \alpha + \beta + \gamma - 180°$$

The angle $\gamma = \angle LMR$ can be computed from the coordinates of the known points $L(x_1, y_1)$, $M(x_2, y_2)$ and $R(x_3, y_3)$ with the calculator and the conversion to polar coordinates $(R \rightarrow P)$. The diameters a and b are obtained from

$$a = \frac{s}{\sin \alpha} \quad \text{and} \quad b = \frac{r}{\sin \beta}.$$

In Fig. 2 we have $\delta' = \delta = \angle MRP$. With this, the coordinates of P can be computed by polar attachment to the segment MR. If δ is a right angle, then B coincides with P. If δ is an obtuse angle, then B lies between A and P (Fig. 3) and it still holds that $\delta' = \delta$.

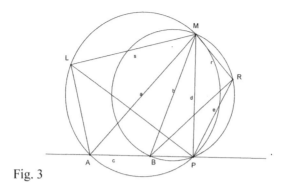

Fig. 3

If $\alpha + \beta + \gamma - 180° < 0$, then A lies between P and B (Fig. 4) or P between B and A (Fig. 5):

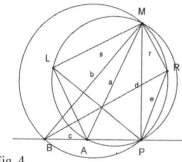

Fig. 4

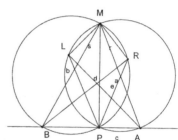

Fig. 5

In the cases of Fig. 4 and Fig. 5, it holds that $\delta = 180 - \delta'$ and $\mu < 0$. So that δ in these cases is calculated as an obtuse angle, we endow side c with the sign of μ:

$$c = \frac{\mu}{|\mu|} \sqrt{a^2 + b^2 - 2ab\cos\mu}$$

and compute δ with the law of cosines:

$$\delta = \arccos \frac{b^2 + c^2 - a^2}{2 \cdot b \cdot c} \qquad a = \frac{s}{\sin\alpha}$$

$$b = \frac{r}{\sin\beta} \qquad c = \frac{r \cdot \sin(\beta + \delta)}{\sin\beta}$$

The coordinates of $P(x, y)$ are finally obtained with the calculator by converting from polar coordinates to rectangular $(P \to R)$ from the calculated values $e = PR$ and δ and the coordinates of R and M.

172

V. Solution of Bronstein (Handbook of Mathematics)

With the angle $\delta = \angle MRP$ and the distance $e = PR$, the coordinates of the new point P can be computed through polar attachment to the known segment RM (cf. Section 3).

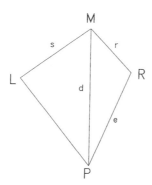

In case the angle δ (as in the drawing) is obtuse, one obtains from the Arctangent (see below) on the calculator the negative supplementary angle of δ. That means δ must be replaced by $180° - |\delta|$ whenever δ is negative. With $\varepsilon = \angle MLP$, $\alpha = \angle LPM$, $\beta = \angle RPM$ and $\gamma = \angle LMR$, one obtains the following formulas:

$$\varepsilon + \delta = 360° - (\alpha + \beta + \gamma) = \tau \qquad \varepsilon = \tau - \delta \qquad \sin\varepsilon = \sin\tau\cos\delta - \cos\tau\sin\delta$$

$$\sin\varepsilon = \frac{d}{s}\sin\alpha \qquad \sin\delta = \frac{d}{r}\sin\beta \qquad \frac{\sin\varepsilon}{\sin\delta} = \frac{r\cdot\sin\alpha}{s\cdot\sin\beta}$$

$$\sin\tau\cot\delta - \cos\tau = \frac{r\cdot\sin\alpha}{s\cdot\sin\beta} \qquad \cot\delta = \frac{r\cdot\sin\alpha}{s\cdot\sin\beta\cdot\sin\tau} + \cot\tau$$

$$\cot\delta = \frac{r\cdot\sin\alpha + s\cdot\sin\beta\cdot\cos\tau}{s\cdot\sin\beta\cdot\sin\tau} \qquad \tan\delta = \frac{s\cdot\sin\beta\cdot\sin\tau}{r\cdot\sin\alpha + s\cdot\sin\beta\cdot\cos\tau}$$

$$e = \frac{r\cdot\sin(\beta+\delta)}{\sin\beta}$$

If P lies on the circle LMR, then $\tau = 180°$ and $\sin\tau = 0$. In this case δ is undetermined.

VI. Concluding Remarks

Although the treatment of resection in the 10th grade trigonometry block is certainly desirable, it is not always possible due to time constraints. It has proven to be helpful in surveying if at least the teacher can double check the reliability of the measured lengths with the method of resection when the necessary angles have been measured. A BASIC-program for a PC or a programmable calculator (e.g., Sharp PC-E220) can easily be created with the help of the above formulas. It is a good idea to write and test such a program for oneself.

What Does "Anthroposophy-based" Mean in Mathematics Instruction?

Markus v. Schwanenflügel

The publications of the Pedagogical Research Center in Kassel are designed to give our colleagues inspiration for their teaching by describing concrete examples that have been successful in the classroom, and most importantly, to do this for the content prescribed for the Waldorf curriculum. That is a intentionally pragmatic aim; however, generally speaking, neither the problems of creating and developing a lesson plan, nor the Waldorf lesson plan, nor yet the so-called anthroposophic questions are at the center of the discussion – for the most part they are only mentioned in passing, or in side comments. The choice of contents and method is not thoroughly explained. The present essay attempts to provide a view into the thought process of a teacher, who, as all teachers, is repeated asked to justify and explain his lessons to colleagues, teachers, and increasingly also to students – the clients should know why the teacher plans certain things for them to happen in a certain way.

In the subsequent pages, the reader will not find any complete, and final arguments that are meant to close the book on the subject – rather the opposite: it is simply to encourage inquiry into one essential aspect of the Waldorf curriculum. Often a discussion about teaching will be ended by a comment that certain content or a certain method is "anthroposophy-based," because this argument is indisputable in a certain sense. But perhaps the discussion should or could really begin at precisely this point. The Waldorf curriculum and its justification are namely not completed entities.

The Waldorf pedagogy is based on the anthroposophic principles developed by *Rudolf Steiner*. Its subject is the research and description of the key principles of the development of the human being, in all levels of its existence. A key result of the research of Rudolf Steiner is that there is a kind of template of the stages and phases of development that the human being experiences sequentially at particular ages. The development of an individual human being can of course differ significantly from this template, but it portrays the general ideal. As such, it is sensible and possible to develop a general study of the human being and, based on that, a *universal* curriculum for *all* students, that takes into consideration, or rather supports, this "ideal development". This is what lies behind the comments, when comparing with other pedagogies, that the Waldorf approach is "anthroposophy-based". Strictly speaking, what this means is this: the choice of content and method is made in relation to the principles of a universal human development, it considers the individual developmental steps and phases and encourages them; contents and methods are chosen to be age-specific, leading, for example, to learning groups that are homogenous in age, the grades [21].

Even the mathematics curriculum traces its Waldorf-specific elements primarily back to suggestions and instructions from *Rudolf Steiner* that he gave at the time of the founding and establish-

---

[21] Naturally, the knowledge of the steps of development and the possibilities for influence do not relieve the teacher of his decision of what to do or not do. How he decides depends on the hierarchy of his aims, or on the way he understands his task as an educator. For questions concerning the genesis of the curriculum of the Waldorf schools, the reader is referred to the essay of Christoph Gögelein: "Geschichte und Prinzipien des 'Lehrplans' der Waldorfschule – zur Lehrplankonstitution der Pädagogik Rudolf Steiners" (Gögelein).

ment of the first Waldorf school. Through examination of a series of citations from *Rudolf Steiner* concerning mathematics, or rather, mathematical instruction[22], I would like to give an example of how to determine what content and methods of the Waldorf-curriculum are anthroposophy-based, and which are not.

We begin with an excerpt from the weekly teacher conferences with Rudolf Steiner. This one concerns mathematics instruction in the 10 grade:

> X: *In algebra, exponents and roots, geometric drawing and and the computation of areas. We also did simple equations, equations with multiple unknowns, quadratic equations, and the figuring of the circumference and arc of a circle.*
>
> *Dr. Steiner*: You could also teach them the concept of π. When you teach that, it is not important that you teach them about the theories of decimal numbers. They can learn the number π to just one decimal place.
>
> X: *We study the number π by looking at the perimeters of inner and outer regular polygons.*
>
> *Dr. Steiner*: What lines do the children know?
>
> X: *Last year we studied the ellipse, hyperbola and parabola from a geometrical perspective.*
>
> *Dr. Steiner*: Then, the children will need to learn the basics of plane trigonometry. I think that would be enough for now. How far did you come in descriptive geometry?
>
> X: *The children learned about interpenetrating planes and surfaces. The children could certainly solve problems involving one triangle penetrated by another. They can also find the point of intersection of a line with a plane.*
>
> *Dr. Steiner*: Perhaps that is not necessary. You should actually begin with orthogonal projections, that is, from a point. You should go through the presentation of a plane as a plane, and not as a triangle.
>
> You should then go to the theory of planes and intersection of two planes and then, perhaps, to the basics of projective geometry. It is important to teach children about the concepts of duality, but you need to teach them only the basic things.
>
> X: *In trigonometry, wouldn't it be necessary to go into logarithms?*
>
> *Dr. Steiner*: What, they don't understand logarithms yet? You must do that in mathematics, it belongs there. They would know only the basic concepts of sine, cosine and tangent, you need to say only a few sentences about that. They should learn only a couple of the relationships, for instance: $\sin^2 + \cos^2 = 1$, but they should understand that visually.
>
> X: *Should the goal be to teach logarithms in the ninth grade?*
>
> *Dr. Steiner*: They should know enough about logarithms to be able to perform simple logarithmic computations[23].

So, in connection with the question of what should be covered in the 10th grade, *Rudolf Steiner* names trigonometry as the allotted task, without reference to his earlier comments, or to re-

---

[22]A publication that is very useful and stimulating for the mathematics teacher is printed by the Pädagogische Forschungsstelle, entitled: "Rudolf Steiner zur Mathematik. Eine Sammlung von Zitaten aus dem Gesamtwerk" 2 Volumes, Stuttgart 1994 (PF94

[23]From: Konferenzen mit den Lehrern (GA 300/2, 4th Edition, 1975) Stuttgart, Friday, June 17, 1921 pp. 24f.

marks of the other conference participants. Later he names the trigonometric functions and "$\sin^2 + \cos^2 = 1$ as visually as possible." The reference to logarithms is probably due to the fact that, at the time, problems in trigonometry were often solved with the help of logarithms.

The above excerpt from the conferences is meant to be a typical example of many such quotes from *Rudolf Steiner*, in which he offers *without any justification* specifics as to *what* is to be taught in each grade. From the tone in which the remarks are formulated, one could conclude that these remarks concern topics that would also normally be suitable in 10th grade mathematics instruction at the public schools.

A few weeks later the topic returns to the 10th grade, when Steiner first makes reference to the practices used at Austrian schools:

> *Dr. Steiner*: The Austrian schools have only very few periods of mathematics. Three in the 4th, 5th and sixth grade and two in the seventh and eighth. If you work in these periods so that you correctly distribute the material you have to cover during the time available, the children will get the most from your instruction. These are children of fifteen or sixteen years of age.
>
> Thus, in geometry, if you can see that the children have the basic concepts, including the law of duality and perspective geometry, so that the children are perplexed and amazed and have some interest in what you say about some of the figures, then you will have achieved everything that you can.
>
> Have you begun with descriptive geometry yet?
>
> *X: I have done the constructions with a point and a line, Cavalieri's perspective and shadow construction, so that the children have an idea of them. Now we are only doing shadow construction. Then, we will do technical drawing. We have done relatively little of that.*
>
> *Dr. Steiner*: Then, you should do mechanical drawing including trajectory, simple machines, and trigonometry. Trajectory is better if you treat it with equations. Do the children understand parabolic equations? If you develop concrete examples, then you do not need to go into detail there. From a pedagogical perspective the whole treatment of a trajectory is only so that the children learn parabolic equations and understand parabolas. The coinciding of reality with mathematical equations is the goal you need to strive for.
>
> "Philosophy begins with awe" is partially incorrect. In teaching, awe must come at the end of a block, whereas in philosophy it is at the beginning. You need to direct the children toward having awe. They need something that will completely occupy them. They need to understand that it is something that, in the presence of its greatness, even Novalis would fall on his knees... [24]

In this citation as well, *Rudolf Steiner* develops, from his view over the subjects (and out beyond their borders as well) – with the public school curriculum fully in view – "didactic ideas", in what sequence and in what context certain content could or should most sensibly be treated. If these ideas are adopted, it often happens that a deepening of the individual subjects and simultaneously

---

[24]From: Konferenzen mit den Lehrern (GA 300/2, 4th Edition 1975) Stuttgart, Sunday, September 11, 1921, pp. 42–44.

a sometimes very surprising integration emerges of very different subjects or, as we would say today, multidisciplinary instruction.[25] A further effect of this kind of "suggestion" and also an explicit aim of *Rudolf Steiner* is that the teachers operate as economically as possible, in the sense that the students learn as much as possible, as robustly as possible, in as short a time as possible.

Viewing seemingly disparate things in combination and revealing relationships is one of Rudolf Steiner's goals. In this, a methodological principle could be recognized that is independent of the age of the student, and which, if used appropriately, can lead to an improvement of the school, because it encourages a rich, holistic learning experience.

Rudolf Steiner repeatedly gives suggestions for improving instruction. For example, in the comment above, that awe should come at the end of a working phase, he notes how the view attained upon reaching the mountaintop after an arduous climb can motivate to ask further questions and to learn more.[26] Such suggestions are very useful. They spring from the subject matter itself, however. In particular, Rudolf Steiner here again has made no reference to age or to the developmental situation of the 16-year old youths (10th grade).[27]

A further example of methodological suggestions of this kind can be given:

> Having gone through the stage of spontaneous activity, which was followed by an appreciation of the descriptive element, the pupil approaching the twelfth year is ready for what could be called the explanatory approach. Now cause and effect enter the general considerations and content can be given which will stretch the powers of reasoning.
>
> Throughout these stages the mathematical aspects in all their manifold forms need to be presented, naturally in a way appropriate to the pupil's age. The mathematical element, such as it is taught in arithmetic and geometry, is liable to cause quite special difficulties to a teacher. Before the ninth year, this work is introduced in its simpler forms, to be subsequently expanded – for the child is well able to take in a great deal if one knows how to proceed in the right ways. Now, it is a fact that all mathematical content which is taught throughout the entire time spent at school must also be presented in a thoroughly artistic and imaginative way. By all kinds of means the teacher must contrive to introduce the arithmetical and geometrical content artistically and here, too, between the ninth and tenth year he has to go over to a descriptive method.

---

[25] No fundamental topic can be adequately covered by remaining entirely *within* one of the usual subjects, particularly not if you want to take into consideration the perspective of the students as learning subjects. See: (Holzkamp93): "Lernen – subjektwissenschaftliche Grundlegung". A particularly poignant example of Rudolf Steiner's is the 3rd course in the natural sciences, "Das Verhältnis der verschiedenen naturwissenschaftlichen Gebiete zur Astronomie" (GA 323), in which he undertakes to show that one cannot study embryology without studying astronomy: "...Because that which is revealed to you by embryology is nothing more that the polar opposite of that which is revealed to you by astronomy..." These three courses in the natural sciences were held for the teachers of the first Waldorf school.

[26] In start contrast to this is the concept of a lesson that begins with an exciting, "captivating" point of departure, but, at the end, fails to provide a substantial, motivating result that speaks to the students: after the fascination at the outset the – mostly subconscious – disappointment at the end is just that much greater; by the third time, the trick doesn't work any longer.

[27] An anthroposophical basis for this reference and for the two preceding citations might well exist. It would have to be researched, however. It does not suffice as proof, namely, that one, for example, observes that the students gain interest in the material. Here we are concerned with the question as to what indicates whether or not certain content or methods are anthroposophy-based.

The pupil has to be taught how to observe angles, triangles, quadrilaterals, and so on, through a descriptive method. Proofs should not enter the work before the twelfth year.

A boring math teacher will achieve extremely little, if anything at all, whereas a teacher, inspired by this subject, will succeed in making it into a stimulating and exhilarating experience for his pupils. For, after all, it is by grace of mathematics that, fundamentally, we are able to experience the harmonies of ideal space. If a teacher can wax enthusiastic over the theorem of Pythagoras or over the inner harmonies between planes and solid bodies, he will bring something into these lessons which is of immense importance for the child, also with regard to its soul development. Through his contributions he will counteract the element of confusion with which life presents us everywhere (...)

Perhaps I may be allowed here a more personal note because it may help to clarify the point I am making. I have a special love for mechanics, not only because of its objective value, but very much for personal reasons. And I owe this love of mechanics to the enthusiasm for this subject displayed by one of my teachers at Vienna University — for such things live on into later life. This teacher glowed with excitement when searching for the resultants from given components. It was so interesting to witness the joy with which he was looking for the resultants and with which he would take them apart again in order to fit them back into their components. While doing this, he almost jumped and danced from one end of the blackboard to the other until, full of glee, he would finally call out the formula he had found, such as: $c^2 = a^2 + b^2$. Captivated by his findings, which he had written on the board, he would look around at his audience with a benign smile which in itself was enough to kindle enthusiasm for analytical mechanics, a subject which usually hardly evokes such feelings in people. It is really important that mathematics, which is taught in its various forms and aspects right through the school, should pour out, as it were, its own special substance over all the pupils.[28]

This citation is a good example of many other similar indications in which *Rudolf Steiner* makes it clear that it is often not so much a matter of content as it is a matter of the teacher's methods and artistic approach, indeed, in what tone (with enthusiasm, etc) he teaches. It is clear that the assessment of these methodological indications depends on what the goals of mathematical instruction are in the first place. That which is here presented as essential to good mathematics teaching is indeed for many teachers just a convenient side effect that indeed has little or nothing to do with the learning of specific mathematical topics or skills (see footnote 1).

At this point I would like to return to the paragraph in the first quote, in which *Rudolf Steiner* suggests "the theory of planes and the intersection of two planes" and "the basics of projective geometry" as content for the 10th grade. This is an example of a number of suggestions whose significance is only revealed when it is understood in combination with *Rudolf Steiner's* remarks from totally different contexts. From them it emerges that he regards mathematics, or the act of doing mathematics, and specifically, the engagement with *this* area of mathematics (projective geometry) as having essential significance for the the development of the whole human being, as

---

[28]From: Die gesunde Entwicklung des Menschenwesens, (GA 303), Tuesday, January 3, 1922 pp. 227–229.

well as for all of humanity. On this point, citation should be made from two lectures in Stuttgart and in Amsterdam in 1921:

> If only the path could be taken from the usual analytical approach of mathematics to the approach of projective mathematics and beyond, if the idea, that I presented here based on the curves with which one must leave space, could be more cultivated – then it would not be so difficult to penetrate forward with the imagination. It is entirely a question of inner spiritual courage. And this inner spiritual courage is what is needed for today's research.[29]
>
> This spiritual condition of meditation and concentration must be the exact same as that which one has when solving problems in geometry or mathematics generally. In the same way that one is fully aware of his will acting in the innermost of his soul in constructing the figures, or in looking for some algebraic or other type of relationship, so must one remain fully aware of the content of his consciousness during this meditation upon easily conceived ideas. It is therefore of great importance that those who wish to be spiritual scientists in the pure sense should actually, at least to a certain degree, be trained mathematically, and indeed to such a degree that they are accustomed to the manner of thinking about mathematical problems.
>
> If I might perhaps allude to a personal experience, it would be the following. I always remember, when I am busy with problems of spiritual science, problems that can be quite difficult, escaping you even once you have them – I always remember that event which decades ago, perhaps 40 years ago, helped to get back on track, that I will now characterize. It was the moment, where I could first grasp the strange fact in synthetic geometry (we will not now delve into the justification of this statement), that from the axioms of synthetic geometry, the point on a line that is infinitely far to the right side is the same as the point that is infinitely far on the left side. It was not so much this mathematical fact, but rather the whole way of thinking, the whole way in which this truth is obtained from the axioms of synthetic geometry, of projective geometry. – I mention it here only to draw attention to the way in which this same state of mind, this same way of letting the consciousness work, is needed, in order for what I call meditation and concentration to take place. [30]

With this recommendation of "mathematics as preparation for spirit-knowledge,"[31] a dimension of mathematics is addressed that is very inspiring for the teacher, and can be helpful in shaping a mathematics lesson that will serve the students long beyond their time in school.

Surely one can say that it would be good if the young person can be introduced in this way to the nature of mathematical discovery and yet it is once again an aspect that is not at all age-specific.

If one understands the development of the human being in the first years as a stepwise process of incarnation that can take place too fast or too slow, too strongly or too weakly, then the following

---

[29] From: Das Verhältnis der verschiedenen naturwissenschaftlichen Gebiete zur Astronomie, (GA 323, 2nd Edition 1983) p. 335.

[30] From: Philosophie und Anthroposophie (in: Das Goetheanum, July 4, 1943, 22. Jahrg. Nr. 27) Amsterdam, March 1, 1921 pp. 210 f.

[31] This is the title of a collection of essays from Louis Locher-Ernst (Locher 73), that are a treasure of inspiration for deepening the teaching of mathematics.

remarks of *Rudolf Steiner* give viewpoints for a certain approach in teaching that one can call anthroposophy-based; however, it is not geared towards one or another age level:

> *(If the ego is too strongly or too weakly bound to the rest of the organization):* we can do something about either extreme, by acquainting ourselves with the means which can cope with such conditions, and these are as follows. Everything that necessitates forming visualizations of figures and of space, like geometry and arithmetic, contributes in instruction and education to the result that the ego settles properly into the organization when the child forms such visualizations and digests them. So do those elements of speech that lean toward music: rhythm, recitation and the like. Music, especially the training of memory for music, has a most beneficent effect upon a child with a tendency to such instability.
>
> Those are the means with which we must work upon a child whose ego does not seem to want to enter the organization properly, and who therefore might easily remain a victim of uncontrolled enthusiasms. When, on the other hand, we notice that the child is becoming too materialistic, that the ego tends to become too dependent on the body, we need only have him draw, physically, those geometrical forms that are ordinarily grasped rather by thought. In this way we create the counterpoise to educate in the right way, provided the subjects of instruction are properly employed.(...) And again, through much drawing and working with pictures, the ego can easily be lifted out of the organization, with consequences as set forth. When a child shows signs of instability as a result of such work, or perhaps even through writing, the remedy is to have him interpret the meaning of what he has drawn, have him think, for instance, of something in connection with the rosette he has drawn, or admire the forms of the letters of the alphabet, and then project them into his consciousness. While mere writing and drawing take the child out of himself, as it were, the observation of what he has drawn and written immerses him in himself, brings him back again into himself.[32]

The suggestion is given for the span of time prior to the 14th year of life, although it probably holds true after that as well. But surely the possibility of influencing the incarnation process of the children through such differentiation in instruction decreases, the older the children get.

There are, however, still deeper questions that could hinder us in naively trying to "implement" such suggestions from *Rudolf Steiner*:

- How does one recognize when an incarnation is too strong (deep) in childhood, and when one is too weak or shallow?

- Why shouldn't each human being simply incarnate how he wants to or how his constitution provides?

- What does 'incarnated' even mean for the being of a human, and for humanity, the earth, the cosmos?

---

[32]From: Supersensible Physiology and Balance in Teaching, Stuttgart, Wednesday, September 22, 1920; Anthroposophic Press, New York 1945

Shouldn't I restrain from consciously "intervening helpfully" in the incarnation process of a student until these questions (and many others resulting from these) are answered?

The following quote is typical of those in which Rudolf Steiner explicitly refers to a certain age and a certain point of development in the human biography:

> The opinion that the child ought to develop the faculty of independent judgement at as early an age as possible, should be abandoned. From the seventh to the fourteenth year it is essential to amass a rich store of memories for the purposes of life, in order that when the astral body is born, as ripe and rich a content of soul as possible shall be produced. Only then should the power of judgement begin to be exercised. The earlier method used in schools which let the "one times one" be learned by heart, that is : $1 \cdot 1 = 1$, and so on, being a matter of actual memorizing, is decidedly preferable to the abstract method at present in vogue of demonstrating the "one times one" with red and white beads on the abacus. This method is decidedly harmful. The same principle applies here as in the case of the young child; it understands language long before it can speak itself. Thus one should only want to let a child exercise its judgement when it has achieved a good memory capacity for the etheric body and has developed certain residual tendencies and habits.[33]

The actual reasons, however, he offers elsewhere:

> In this second period, around the ninth or tenth year, Ahriman grips the human being, namely, and forms a kind of balance with his current to the Lucifer current. We can only accomplish the greatest favor to Ahriman if, at exactly this moment, we educate the intellect in the growing child, which is directed toward the outer sensory world; if we say to ourselves: the child must be trained at this time in such a way that it can, above all else, come to its own, independent judgement as much as possible. – You know that I am speaking of an educational principle that is quite commonly expressed in education these days. Developing independence, particularly in these years, is almost universally demanded these days. Calculators are provided so that the children are not even given a chance to learn their times tables properly from memory. This is entirely based on a certain good will of our age towards Ahriman. Our age wishes, unconsciously of course, to raise the children in such a way that Ahriman is cultivated in the human soul as strongly as possible.[34]

Such, therefore, is the reason that *Rudolf Steiner* gives, that he repeatedly warns, not only in connection with mathematics instruction, against fostering or training an independent judgement in children too early. Here he makes an explicit connection to the development of the human being

---

[33]From: Das Prinzip der spirituellen Ökonomie im Zusammenhang mit Wiederverkörperungsfragen, (GA 109/11) Budapest, June 7, 1909, pp. 207 f.

[34]From: Die Welt des Geistes und ihr Hereinragen in das physische Dasein, (GA 150) Augsburg, March 14, 1913, pp. 17 f.

and/or to the development of its members. The reference to Ahriman and Lucifer highlights the importance of this indication.[35]

In contrast to the other preceding examples, an anthroposophic basis in the strict sense is given here for a specific approach in mathematics instruction at a certain age.

Such guidance is rare when it comes to mathematics instruction. In my opinion, it is missing entirely for instruction beyond puberty (from the 14th year on).

What, now, is the situation of our knowledge as Waldorf teachers regarding such justification? Are we, *ourselves*, in a position to give such a justification on the basis of our own research or that research of our colleagues? Has, e.g., the question been pursued as to how emphasizing judgement or memorization too early actually impacts the children's development? Or can we only, if we are honest, still to this day only *believe* these indications of Rudolf Steiner or *cite* them in a more or less paraphrased form?

In my opinion, the latter is the case, from which the following tasks arise for work on a broader curriculum for the subject of mathematics:

- First, the identification of Rudolf Steiner's suggestions for mathematics instruction that are anthroposophy-based in the strict sense, and seeing to what extent we can represent them as foundational knowledge or discoveries.

- Associated with that, the publication of materials relevant for the teaching of mathematics that specifically address the anthroposophy-based indications of Rudolf Steiner and further elucidate these.

- Publication of discoveries and research results that contain the anthroposophy-based choice of material and methods.[36]

Anyone who has suggestions or advice or who would like to take part in this work is encouraged to please contact either the Pedagogical Research Center in Kassel or the author personally.

---

[35] It should not be overlooked that the quote begins with by pointing out that this concerns the balance of two currents. A fact is described that does not necessarily entail a certain decision. Why then is early judgement harmful, actually? Again it can be made clear that a careful justification of the lesson always includes or presupposes a clarification of the goals. See footnote 1.

[36] These tasks can naturally be transferred to other subjects as well.

Index

29279704R00104

Made in the USA
Middletown, DE
13 February 2016